WALKING THROUGH

FIRE

A Study from First Peter on the Trial of Your Faith

JOHN GOETSCH

First published in 2012 by Striving Together Publications, a ministry of Lancaster Baptist Church, Lancaster, CA 93535. Striving Together Publications is committed to providing tried, trusted, and proven books that will further equip local churches to carry out the Great Commission. Your comments and suggestions are valued.

Striving Together Publications
4020 E. Lancaster Blvd.
Lancaster, CA 93535
800.201.7748

Cover design by Andrew Jones
Layout by Craig Parker
Special thanks to our proofreaders

The author and publication team have put forth every effort to give proper credit to quotes and thoughts that are not original with the author. It is not our intent to claim originality with any quote or thought that could not readily be tied to an original source.

ISBN 978-1-59894-197-5
Printed in the United States of America

Table of Contents

An Author's Pilgrimage

Key Verses

MATTHEW 26:31–35

31 Then saith Jesus unto them, All ye shall be offended because of me this night: for it is written, I will smite the shepherd, and the sheep of the flock shall be scattered abroad.

32 But after I am risen again, I will go before you into Galilee.

33 Peter answered and said unto him, Though all men shall be offended because of thee, yet will I never be offended.

34 Jesus said unto him, Verily I say unto thee, That this night, before the cock crow, thou shalt deny me thrice.

35 Peter said unto him, Though I should die with thee, yet will I not deny thee. Likewise also said all the disciples.

Overview

A faith that cannot be tested cannot be trusted. Most of us, like Peter, would probably say that our relationship with Jesus Christ is good. We would say that we love the Lord, enjoy attending church, and do our best to be faithful in our everyday attitudes and actions. But while a relationship with Christ is established in a moment of faith, to be strong it must be built over years of faithfulness.

Before we get to the book of 1 Peter, we want to look at this critical moment in Peter's life when his faith was put to the test. Every believer's walk will be defined in these moments of crisis. How we do will determine our futures.

Lesson Theme

Peter was about to have his faith tested. Unfortunately, he failed. Through this experience, however, God built this man to a place of great usefulness. In this first lesson we will discover what gave Peter the right to speak to us about "walking through fire." God wants to use us, but like Peter we must learn from our failures.

Introduction

_____

_____

_____

I. A _____ Exclamation

A. A _____ *prediction*

PROVERBS 16:18

18 Pride goeth before destruction, and an haughty spirit before a fall.

1 CORINTHIANS 10:12

12 Wherefore let him that thinketh he standeth take heed lest he fall.

PROVERBS 25:14

14 Whoso boasteth himself of a false gift is like clouds and wind without rain.

B. A _____ *practice*

MATTHEW 26:36–44

36 Then cometh Jesus with them unto a place called Gethsemane, and saith unto the disciples, Sit ye here, while I go and pray yonder.

37 And he took with him Peter and the two sons of Zebedee, and began to be sorrowful and very heavy.

38 Then saith he unto them, My soul is exceeding sorrowful, even unto death: tarry ye here, and watch with me.

39 And he went a little further, and fell on his face, and prayed, saying, O my Father, if it be possible, let this cup pass from me: nevertheless not as I will, but as thou wilt.

40 And he cometh unto the disciples, and findeth them asleep, and saith unto Peter, What, could ye not watch with me one hour?

41 Watch and pray, that ye enter not into temptation: the spirit indeed is willing, but the flesh is weak.

42 He went away again the second time, and prayed, saying, O my Father, if this cup may not pass away from me, except I drink it, thy will be done.

43 And he came and found them asleep again: for their eyes were heavy.

44 And he left them, and went away again, and prayed the third time, saying the same words.

JOHN 15:5

5 …for without me ye can do nothing.

2 CORINTHIANS 3:5

5 Not that we are sufficient of ourselves to think any thing as of ourselves; but our sufficiency is of God.

1 CORINTHIANS 15:10

10 But by the grace of God I am what I am: and his grace which was bestowed upon me was not in vain; but I labored more abundantly than they all: yet not I, but the grace of God which was with me.

C. A _____ *panic*

MATTHEW 26:45–56

45 Then cometh he to his disciples, and saith unto them, Sleep on now, and take your rest: behold, the hour is at hand, and the Son of man is betrayed into the hands of sinners.

46 Rise, let us be going: behold, he is at hand that doth betray me.

47 And while he yet spake, lo, Judas, one of the twelve, came, and with him a great multitude with swords and staves, from the chief priests and elders of the people.

48 Now he that betrayed him gave them a sign, saying, Whomsoever I shall kiss, that same is he: hold him fast.

49 And forthwith he came to Jesus, and said, Hail, master; and kissed him.

50 And Jesus said unto him, Friend, wherefore art thou come? Then came they, and laid hands on Jesus, and took him.

51 And, behold, one of them which were with Jesus stretched out his hand, and drew his sword, and struck a servant of the high priest's, and smote off his ear.

52 Then said Jesus unto him, Put up again thy sword into his place: for all they that take the sword shall perish with the sword.

53 Thinkest thou that I cannot now pray to my Father, and he shall presently give me more than twelve legions of angels?

54 But how then shall the scriptures be fulfilled, that thus it must be?

55 In that same hour said Jesus to the multitudes, Are ye come out as against a thief with swords and staves for to take me? I sat daily with you teaching in the temple, and ye laid no hold on me.

56 But all this was done, that the scriptures of the prophets might be fulfilled. Then all the disciples forsook him, and fled.

ECCLESIASTES 5:4–7

4   When thou vowest a vow unto God, defer not to pay it; for he hath no pleasure in fools: pay that which thou hast vowed.

5   Better is it that thou shouldest not vow, than that thou shouldest vow and not pay.

6   Suffer not thy mouth to cause thy flesh to sin; neither say thou before the angel, that it was an error: wherefore should God be angry at thy voice, and destroy the work of thine hands?

7   For in the multitude of dreams and many words there are also divers vanities: but fear thou God.

II. A _____ Examination

1 THESSALONIANS 3:5

5   For this cause, when I could no longer forbear, I sent to know your faith, lest by some means the tempter have tempted you, and our labour be in vain.

2 CORINTHIANS 11:3

3   But I fear, lest by any means, as the serpent beguiled Eve through his subtilty, so your minds should be corrupted from the simplicity that is in Christ.

1 PETER 5:8

8   Be sober, be vigilant; because your adversary the devil, as a roaring lion, walketh about, seeking whom he may devour.

A. A _____ crowd

MATTHEW 26:57–68

57   And they that had laid hold on Jesus led him away to Caiaphas the high priest, where the scribes and the elders were assembled.

58 But Peter followed him afar off unto the high priest's palace, and went in, and sat with the servants, to see the end.

59 Now the chief priests, and elders, and all the council, sought false witness against Jesus, to put him to death;

60 But found none: yea, though many false witnesses came, yet found they none. At the last came two false witnesses,

61 And said, This fellow said, I am able to destroy the temple of God, and to build it in three days.

62 And the high priest arose, and said unto him, Answerest thou nothing? what is it which these witness against thee?

63 But Jesus held his peace. And the high priest answered and said unto him, I adjure thee by the living God, that thou tell us whether thou be the Christ, the Son of God.

64 Jesus saith unto him, Thou hast said: nevertheless I say unto you, Hereafter shall ye see the Son of man sitting on the right hand of power, and coming in the clouds of heaven.

65 Then the high priest rent his clothes, saying, He hath spoken blasphemy; what further need have we of witnesses? behold, now ye have heard his blasphemy.

66 What think ye? They answered and said, He is guilty of death.

67 Then did they spit in his face, and buffeted him; and others smote him with the palms of their hands,

68 Saying, Prophesy unto us, thou Christ, Who is he that smote thee?

JOHN 15:18–19

18 If the world hate you, ye know that it hated me before it hated you.

19 If ye were of the world, the world would love his own: but because ye are not of the world, but I have chosen you out of the world, therefore the world hateth you.

1 Corinthians 2:14
14 But the natural man receiveth not the things of the Spirit of God: for they are foolishness unto him: neither can he know them, because they are spiritually discerned.

1 Corinthians 1:18
18 For the preaching of the cross is to them that perish foolishness…

John 1:11
11 He came unto his own, and his own received him not.

John 3:19–20
19 And this is the condemnation, that light is come into the world, and men loved darkness rather than light, because their deeds were evil.
20 For every one that doeth evil hateth the light, neither cometh to the light, lest his deeds should be reproved.

B. A _____ *connection*
Matthew 26:69–73
69 Now Peter sat without in the palace: and a damsel came unto him, saying, Thou also wast with Jesus of Galilee.
70 But he denied before them all, saying, I know not what thou sayest.
71 And when he was gone out into the porch, another maid saw him, and said unto them that were there, This fellow was also with Jesus of Nazareth.

72 And again he denied with an oath, I do not know the man.

73 And after a while came unto him they that stood by, and said to Peter, Surely thou also art one of them; for thy speech bewrayeth thee.

EPHESIANS 5:18

18 And be not drunk with wine, wherein is excess; but be filled with the Spirit.

C. A _____ cover-up

MATTHEW 26:74

74 Then began he to curse and to swear, saying, I know not the man...

1 CORINTHIANS 10:12

12 Wherefore let him that thinketh he standeth take heed lest he fall.

JAMES 1:14–15

14 But every man is tempted, when he is drawn away of his own lust, and enticed.

15 Then when lust hath conceived, it bringeth forth sin: and sin, when it is finished, bringeth forth death.

III. A _____ Exposure

1 SAMUEL 16:7

7 But LORD said unto Samuel, Look not on his countenance, or on the height of his stature; because I have refused him: for the LORD seeth not as man seeth; for man looketh on the outward appearance, but the LORD looketh on the heart.

JEREMIAH 17:10

10   I the LORD search the heart, I try the reins, even to give every man according to his ways, and according to the fruit of his doings.

PSALM 90:8

8   Thou hast set our iniquities before thee, our secret sins in the light of thy countenance.

PSALM 69:5

5   O God, thou knowest my foolishness; and my sins are not hid from thee.

PSALM 44:20–21

20   If we have forgotten the name of our God, or stretched out our hands to a strange god;
21   Shall not God search this out? for he knoweth the secrets of the heart.

LUKE 12:2–5

2   For there is nothing covered, that shall not be revealed; neither hid, that shall not be known.
3   Therefore whatsoever ye have spoken in darkness shall be heard in the light; and that which ye have spoken in the ear in closets shall be proclaimed upon the housetops.
4   And I say unto you my friends, Be not afraid of them that kill the body, and after that have no more that they can do.
5   But I will forewarn you whom ye shall fear: Fear him, which after he hath killed hath power to cast into hell; yea, I say unto you, Fear him.

HEBREWS 4:13

13   Neither is there any creature that is not manifest in his sight: but all things are naked and opened unto the eyes of him with whom we have to do.

A. A _____

MATTHEW 26:34, 74

34 Jesus said unto him, Verily I say unto thee, That this night, before the cock crow, thou shalt deny me thrice.

74 Then began he to curse and to swear, saying, I know not the man. And immediately the cock crew.

PSALM 119:9–11

9 Wherewithal shall a young man cleanse his way? by taking heed thereto according to thy word.

10 With my whole heart have I sought thee: O let me not wander from thy commandments.

11 Thy word have I hid in mine heart, that I might not sin against thee.

PROVERBS 1:22–25

22 How long, ye simple ones, will ye love simplicity? and the scorners delight in their scorning, and fools hate knowledge?

23 Turn you at my reproof: behold, I will pour out my spirit unto you, I will make known my words unto you.

24 Because I have called, and ye refused; I have stretched out my hand, and no man regarded;

25 But ye have set at nought all my counsel, and would none of my reproof:

PROVERBS 13:13

13 Whoso despiseth the word shall be destroyed: but he that feareth the commandment shall be rewarded.

B. A _____

MATTHEW 26:75

75   *And Peter remembered the word of Jesus, which said unto him, Before the cock crow, thou shalt deny me thrice. And he went out, and wept bitterly.*

GALATIANS 6:7–8

7   *Be not deceived; God is not mocked: for whatsoever a man soweth, that shall he also reap.*

8   *For he that soweth to his flesh shall of the flesh reap corruption; but he that soweth to the Spirit shall of the Spirit reap life everlasting.*

NUMBERS 32:23

23   *But if ye will not do so, behold, ye have sinned against the LORD: and be sure your sin will find you out.*

PROVERBS 28:13

13   *He that covereth his sins shall not prosper: but whoso confesseth and forsaketh them shall have mercy.*

1 JOHN 1:9–10

9   *If we confess our sins, he is faithful and just to forgive us our sins, and to cleanse us from all unrighteousness.*

10   *If we say that we have not sinned, we make him a liar, and his word is not in us.*

IV. A _____ **Example**

PROVERBS 24:16

16   *For a just man falleth seven times, and riseth up again…*

A. A _____ *Saviour*

MARK 16:7

7   But go your way, tell his disciples and Peter that he goeth before you into Galilee: there ye shall see him, as he said unto you.

PSALM 103:8

8   The LORD is merciful and gracious, slow to anger, and plenteous in mercy.

PSALM 103:12

12   As far as the east is from the west, so far hath he removed our transgressions from us.

ISAIAH 43:25

25   I, even I, am he that blotteth out thy transgressions for mine own sake, and will not remember thy sins.

B. A _____ *servant*

ACTS 2:12–16

12   And they were all amazed, and were in doubt, saying one to another, What meaneth this?

13   Others mocking said, These men are full of new wine.

14   But Peter, standing up with the eleven, lifted up his voice, and said unto them, Ye men of Judæa, and all ye that dwell at Jerusalem, be this known unto you, and hearken to my words:

15   For these are not drunken, as ye suppose, seeing it is but the third hour of the day.

16   But this is that which was spoken by the prophet Joel;

2 Corinthians 5:15

15 And that he died for all, that they which live should not henceforth live unto themselves, but unto him which died for them, and rose again.

Romans 12:1

1 I beseech you therefore, brethren, by the mercies of God, that ye present your bodies a living sacrifice, holy, acceptable unto God, which is your reasonable service.

C. A _____ statement.

2 Peter 3:17–18

17 Ye therefore, beloved, seeing ye know these things before, beware lest ye also, being led away with the error of the wicked, fall from your own stedfastness.

18 But grow in grace, and in the knowledge of our Lord and Saviour Jesus Christ. To him be glory both now and for ever. Amen.

Conclusion

_____

_____

_____

Study Questions

1. When do the tests of your faith begin?

2. What can often cause us to fail when we make decisions for Christ?

3. Why do you think people tend to overreact when they fail?

4. When was a time your faith was tested?

5. How will people watching your life be affected by the daily decisions you make for Christ?

6. How can you be better equipped for the devil's attacks?

7. Write out two Bible verses that you could memorize to help you fight off Satan's attacks.

8. What should motivate us to be faithful to God?

Memory Verse

ROMANS 12:1

1   I beseech you therefore, brethren, by the mercies of God, that ye present your bodies a living sacrifice, holy, acceptable unto God, which is your reasonable service.

An Audience's Plight

Key Verses

1 PETER 1:1–2

1   Peter, an apostle of Jesus Christ, to the strangers scattered throughout Pontus, Galatia, Cappadocia, Asia, and Bithynia,
2   Elect according to the foreknowledge of God the Father, through sanctification of the Spirit, unto obedience and sprinkling of the blood of Jesus Christ: Grace unto you, and peace, be multiplied.

Overview

God has a purpose for everything He says and does. The first epistle of Peter was written to people who were going through some difficult times. While some of those adversities were well known, there were also dangers coming that were unknown. The letter was written to help them be triumphant in the trials both now and in the future.

The challenges we face today are not always obvious. We must remember that we are in a battle with an invisible enemy. *"For we wrestle not against flesh and blood, but against principalities, against powers, against the rulers of the darkness of this world, against spiritual wickedness in high places"* (Ephesians 6:12). How we fare in this battle will be determined by how well we are prepared. First Peter is a book that will help us do just that.

Lesson Theme

The first century church had grown very rapidly and Satan is never happy when God's work is progressing. The wicked one was about to unleash a host of fiery darts at these young believers. These relentless attacks would come from multiple sides in an effort to annihilate the pillar and ground of the truth. These believers were going to have to be ready at all times if they were to survive.

The twenty-first century Christian is facing a furious last-minute effort by Satan to destroy God's work. The devil knows that his time is short, and he is determined to make every moment count. This is no time for God's people to relax, but rather to be vigilant. We can be vigilant because *"greater is he that is in you, than he that is in the world"* (1 John 4:4).

Introduction

_____

_____

_____

I. A Scattered _____

ACTS 2:1

1   And when the day of Pentecost was fully come, they were all with one accord in one place.

ACTS 2:44

44 And all that believed were together, and had all things common.

ACTS 2:46

46 And they, continuing daily with one accord in the temple, and breaking bread from house to house, did eat their meat with gladness and singleness of heart.

ACTS 8:1

1   And Saul was consenting unto his death. And at that time there was a great persecution against the church which was at Jerusalem; and they were all scattered abroad throughout the regions of Judaea and Samaria, except the apostles.

ACTS 8:4

4   Therefore they that were scattered abroad went every where preaching the word.

ACTS 11:19–21

19 Now they which were scattered abroad upon the persecution that arose about Stephen travelled as far as

Phenice, and Cyprus, and Antioch, preaching the word to none but unto the Jews only.

20   And some of them were men of Cyprus and Cyrene, which, when they were come to Antioch, spake unto the Grecians, preaching the Lord Jesus.

21   And the hand of the Lord was with them: and a great number believed, and turned unto the Lord.

A. An _____ *audience*

1 PETER 1:1

1   Peter, an apostle of Jesus Christ, to the strangers scattered throughout Pontus, Galatia, Cappadocia, Asia, and Bithynia.

2 TIMOTHY 3:16–17

16   All scripture is given by inspiration of God, and is profitable for doctrine, for reproof, for correction, for instruction in righteousness:

17   That the man of God may be perfect, throughly furnished unto all good works.

B. A _____ *audience*

1 PETER 1:2

2   Elect according to the foreknowledge of God the Father…

JOHN 17:11

11   …Holy Father, keep through thine own name those whom thou hast given me, that they may be one, as we are.

JOHN 17:20–22

20   Neither pray I for these alone, but for them also which shall believe on me through their word;

21 *That they all may be one; as thou, Father, art in me, and I in thee, that they also may be one in us: that the world may believe that thou hast sent me.*

22 *And the glory which thou gavest me I have given them; that they may be one, even as we are one:*

1 CORINTHIANS 12:12–13

12 *For as the body is one, and hath many members, and all the members of that one body, being many, are one body: so also is Christ.*

13 *For by one Spirit are we all baptized into one body, whether we be Jews or Gentiles, whether we be bond or free; and have been all made to drink into one Spirit.*

C. An _____ audience

1 PETER 1:2

2 *…through sanctification of the Spirit, unto obedience and sprinkling of the blood of Jesus Christ: Grace unto you, and peace, be multiplied.*

JOHN 10:28–29

28 *And I give unto them eternal life; and they shall never perish, neither shall any man pluck them out of my hand.*

29 *My Father, which gave them me, is greater than all; and no man is able to pluck them out of my Father's hand.*

JOHN 6:35, 37

35 *And Jesus said unto them, I am the bread of life: he that cometh to me shall never hunger; and he that believeth on me shall never thirst.*

37 *All that the Father giveth me shall come to me; and him that cometh to me I will in no wise cast out.*

2 TIMOTHY 1:12

12 *...for I know whom I have believed, and am persuaded that he is able to keep that which I have committed unto him against that day.*

II. A Sudden _____

A. *A weighty* _____

1 PETER 1:6–7

6   *Wherein ye greatly rejoice, though now for a season, if need be, ye are in heaviness through manifold temptations:*

7   *That the trial of your faith, being much more precious than of gold that perisheth, though it be tried with fire, might be found unto praise and honour and glory at the appearing of Jesus Christ:*

B. *A wrongful* _____

1 PETER 3:13–17

13   *And who is he that will harm you, if ye be followers of that which is good?*

14   *But and if ye suffer for righteousness' sake, happy are ye: and be not afraid of their terror, neither be troubled;*

15   *But sanctify the Lord God in your hearts: and be ready always to give an answer to every man that asketh you a reason of the hope that is in you with meekness and fear:*

16   *Having a good conscience; that, whereas they speak evil of you, as of evildoers, they may be ashamed that falsely accuse your good conversation in Christ.*

17   *For it is better, if the will of God be so, that ye suffer for well doing, than for evil doing.*

C. A wonderful _____

1 PETER 4:12–19

12 Beloved, think it not strange concerning the fiery trial which is to try you, as though some strange thing happened unto you:

13 But rejoice, inasmuch as ye are partakers of Christ's sufferings; that, when his glory shall be revealed, ye may be glad also with exceeding joy.

14 If ye be reproached for the name of Christ, happy are ye; for the spirit of glory and of God resteth upon you: on their part he is evil spoken of, but on your part he is glorified.

15 But let none of you suffer as a murderer, or as a thief, or as an evildoer, or as a busybody in other men's matters.

16 Yet if any man suffer as a Christian, let him not be ashamed; but let him glorify God on this behalf.

17 For the time is come that judgment must begin at the house of God: and if it first begin at us, what shall the end be of them that obey not the gospel of God?

18 And if the righteous scarcely be saved, where shall the ungodly and the sinner appear?

19 Wherefore let them that suffer according to the will of God commit the keeping of their souls to him in well doing, as unto a faithful Creator.

ACTS 5:41

41 And they departed from the presence of the council, rejoicing that they were counted worthy to suffer shame for his name.

ROMANS 8:17

17 And if children, then heirs; heirs of God, and joint-heirs with Christ; if so be that we suffer with him, that we may be also glorified together.

III. A Separating _____

LEVITICUS 10:10
10   And that ye may put difference between holy and unholy, and between unclean and clean.

MATTHEW 5:16
16   Let your light so shine before men, that they may see your good works, and glorify your Father which is in heaven.

2 CORINTHIANS 3:2–3
2   Ye are our epistle written in our hearts, known and read of all men:
3   Forasmuch as ye are manifestly declared to be the epistle of Christ ministered by us, written not with ink, but with the Spirit of the living God; not in tables of stone, but in fleshly tables of the heart.

A. The believer's response to worldly _____
1 PETER 4:4–5
4   Wherein they think it strange that ye run not with them to the same excess of riot, speaking evil of you:
5   Who shall give account to him that is ready to judge the quick and the dead.

1 JOHN 2:15–17
15   Love not the world, neither the things that are in the world. If any man love the world, the love of the Father is not in him.
16   For all that is in the world, the lust of the flesh, and the lust of the eyes, and the pride of life, is not of the Father, but is of the world.
17   And the world passeth away, and the lust thereof: but he that doeth the will of God abideth for ever.

2 CORINTHIANS 6:14–18

14   Be ye not unequally yoked together with unbelievers: for what fellowship hath righteousness with unrighteousness? and what communion hath light with darkness?

15   And what concord hath Christ with Belial? or what part hath he that believeth with an infidel?

16   And what agreement hath the temple of God with idols? for ye are the temple of the living God; as God hath said, I will dwell in them, and walk in them; and I will be their God, and they shall be my people.

17   Wherefore come out from among them, and be ye separate, saith the Lord, and touch not the unclean thing; and I will receive you,

18   And will be a Father unto you, and ye shall be my sons and daughters, saith the Lord Almighty.

EPHESIANS 5:11

11   And have no fellowship with the unfruitful works of darkness, but rather reprove them.

B. The believer's response to wicked _____

1 PETER 2:13–14

13   Submit yourselves to every ordinance of man for the Lord's sake: whether it be to the king, as supreme;

14   Or unto governors, as unto them that are sent by him for the punishment of evildoers, and for the praise of them that do well.

ECCLESIASTES 10:20

20   Curse not the king, no not in thy thought…

ROMANS 13:1

1   Let every soul be subject unto the higher powers. For there is no power but of God: the powers that be are ordained of God.

TITUS 3:1

1   Put them in mind to be subject to principalities and powers, to obey magistrates, to be ready to every good work.

ROMANS 12:19, 21

19   Dearly beloved, avenge not yourselves, but rather give place unto wrath: for it is written, Vengeance is mine; I will repay, saith the Lord.

21   Be not overcome of evil, but overcome evil with good.

IV. A Sincere _____

A. An intimidation from the _____

1 PETER 2:11–12

11   Dearly beloved, I beseech you as strangers and pilgrims, abstain from fleshly lusts, which war against the soul;

12   Having your conversation honest among the Gentiles: that, whereas they speak against you as evildoers, they may by your good works, which they shall behold, glorify God in the day of visitation.

GALATIANS 5:16–17

16   This I say then, Walk in the Spirit, and ye shall not fulfill the lust of the flesh.

17   For the flesh lusteth against the Spirit, and the Spirit against the flesh: and these are contrary the one to the other: so that ye cannot do the things that ye would.

Colossians 3:5–10

5   Mortify therefore your members which are upon the earth; fornication, uncleanness, inordinate affection, evil concupiscence, and covetousness, which is idolatry:

6   For which things' sake the wrath of God cometh on the children of disobedience:

7   In the which ye also walked some time, when ye lived in them.

8   But now ye also put off all these; anger, wrath, malice, blasphemy, filthy communication out of your mouth.

9   Lie not one to another, seeing that ye have put off the old man with his deeds;

10   And have put on the new man, which is renewed in knowledge after the image of him that created him:

B.   An inactivity among the _____

1 Peter 2:16

16   As free, and not using your liberty for a cloke of maliciousness, but as the servants of God.

John 13:17

17   If ye know these things, happy are ye if ye do them.

James 1:21–22

21   Wherefore lay apart all filthiness and superfluity of naughtiness, and receive with meekness the engrafted word, which is able to save your souls.

22   But be ye doers of the word, and not hearers only, deceiving your own selves.

C. An inconsistency in the _____

1 PETER 5:2–3

2   Feed the flock of God which is among you, taking the oversight thereof, not by constraint, but willingly; not for filthy lucre, but of a ready mind;

3   Neither as being lords over God's heritage, but being ensamples to the flock.

ACTS 20:28

28   Take heed therefore unto yourselves, and to all the flock, over the which the Holy Ghost hath made you overseers, to feed the church of God, which he hath purchased with his own blood.

Conclusion

_____

_____

_____

EPHESIANS 6:10–18

10   Finally, my brethren, be strong in the Lord, and in the power of his might.

11   Put on the whole armour of God, that ye may be able to stand against the wiles of the devil.

12   For we wrestle not against flesh and blood, but against principalities, against powers, against the rulers of the darkness of this world, against spiritual wickedness in high places.

13   Wherefore take unto you the whole armour of God, that ye may be able to withstand in the evil day, and having done all, to stand.

14 *Stand therefore, having your loins girt about with truth, and having on the breastplate of righteousness;*

15 *And your feet shod with the preparation of the gospel of peace;*

16 *Above all, taking the shield of faith, wherewith ye shall be able to quench all the fiery darts of the wicked.*

17 *And take the helmet of salvation, and the sword of the Spirit, which is the word of God:*

18 *Praying always with all prayer and supplication in the Spirit, and watching thereunto with all perseverance and supplication for all saints;*

Study Questions

1. What do we need to claim for the challenges we face each day?

2. What did the early believers in Acts learn to expect?

3. In what ways has the devil tried to persecute you?

4. What never changes regardless of our circumstances?

5. Are you willing to suffer for being faithful to God? Why or why not?

6. Why is it crucial that our lives are different from the world?

7. What is often our own worst enemy?

8. How can you keep the world, the flesh, and the devil from defeating you?

Memory Verse

MATTHEW 5:16

16 *Let your light so shine before men, that they may see your good works, and glorify your Father which is in heaven.*

An Amazing Salvation

Key Verses

1 PETER 1:2–5

2   Elect according to the foreknowledge of God the Father, through sanctification of the Spirit, unto obedience and sprinkling of the blood of Jesus Christ: Grace unto you, and peace, be multiplied.

3   Blessed be the God and Father of our Lord Jesus Christ, which according to his abundant mercy hath begotten us again unto a lively hope by the resurrection of Jesus Christ from the dead,

4   To an inheritance incorruptible, and undefiled, and that fadeth not away, reserved in heaven for you,

5   Who are kept by the power of God through faith unto salvation ready to be revealed in the last time.

Overview

While life can get chaotic and often is uncertain, this lesson helps us realize that no matter what happens, our salvation is secure in Christ. When trials come, the devil wants us to think that God has abandoned us or at least is upset with us and that our standing with Him is in jeopardy. This is never the case. Peter is writing to these believers to assure them that while the sea of life may be tumultuous, they are secure in Christ.

Lesson Theme

This lesson emphasizes the wonderful gift of salvation that God has given to us. Having an understanding of our eternal security in Christ makes facing the obstacles of life much easier. We know that we have one living within us who is greater than any adversity we face. Learning to rely on Him during the difficult times is the key to "walking through fire."

Introduction

_____

_____

_____

MARK 8:36–37

36 For what shall it profit a man, if he shall gain the whole world, and lose his own soul?

37 Or what shall a man give in exchange for his soul?

I. A _____ Salvation

JAMES 1:18

18 Of his own will begat he us with the word of truth, that we should be a kind of firstfruits of his creatures.

1 JOHN 4:9–10

9 In this was manifested the love of God toward us, because that God sent his only begotten Son into the world, that we might live through him.

10 Herein is love, not that we loved God, but that he loved us, and sent his Son to be a propitiation for our sins.

A. A fatherly _____

1 PETER 1:2

2 Elect according to the foreknowledge of God the Father...

1 TIMOTHY 2:3–4

3 For this is good and acceptable in the sight of God our Saviour;

4   *Who will have all men to be saved, and to come unto the knowledge of the truth.*

2 PETER 3:9
9   *The Lord is not slack concerning his promise, as some men count slackness; but is longsuffering to us-ward, not willing that any should perish, but that all should come to repentance.*

2 CORINTHIANS 5:15
15   *And that he died for all...*

JOHN 3:16
16   *For God so loved the world, that he gave his only begotten Son, that whosoever believeth in him should not perish, but have everlasting life.*

ROMANS 10:13
13   *For whosoever shall call upon the name of the Lord shall be saved.*

1 CORINTHIANS 2:7
7   *But we speak the wisdom of God in a mystery, even the hidden wisdom, which God ordained before the world unto our glory.*

B. A forethought _____

1 PETER 1:2
2   *...through sanctification of the Spirit...*

ROMANS 8:29
29   *For whom he did foreknow, he also did predestinate to be conformed to the image of his Son...*

2 TIMOTHY 1:9

9 *Who hath saved us, and called us with an holy calling...*

EPHESIANS 1:11–12

11 *In whom also we have obtained an inheritance, being predestinated according to the purpose of him who worketh all things after the counsel of his own will:*

12 *That we should be to the praise of his glory, who first trusted in Christ.*

REVELATION 4:11

11 *Thou art worthy, O Lord, to receive glory and honour and power: for thou hast created all things, and for thy pleasure they are and were created.*

C. A finished _____

1 PETER 1:2

2 *...unto obedience and sprinkling of the blood of Jesus Christ: Grace unto you, and peace, be multiplied.*

TITUS 3:4–7

4 *But after that the kindness and love of God our Saviour toward man appeared,*

5 *Not by works of righteousness which we have done, but according to his mercy he saved us, by the washing of regeneration, and renewing of the Holy Ghost;*

6 *Which he shed on us abundantly through Jesus Christ our Saviour;*

7 *That being justified by his grace, we should be made heirs according to the hope of eternal life.*

EPHESIANS 2:8–9

8   *For by grace are ye saved through faith: and that not of yourselves: it is the gift of God:*

9   *Not of works, lest any man should boast.*

GALATIANS 2:16

16   *Knowing that a man is not justified by the works of the law, but by the faith of Jesus Christ, even we have believed in Jesus Christ, that we might be justified by the faith of Christ, and not by the works of the law: for by the works of the law shall no flesh be justified.*

II. A _____ Salvation

GENESIS 6:5–7

5   *And God saw that the wickedness of man was great in the earth, and that every imagination of the thoughts of his heart was only evil continually.*

6   *And it repented the LORD that he had made man on the earth, and it grieved him at his heart.*

7   *And the LORD said, I will destroy man whom I have created from the face of the earth; both man, and beast, and the creeping thing, and the fowls of the air; for it repenteth me that I have made them.*

PSALM 5:4–6

4   *For thou art not a God that hath pleasure in wickedness: neither shall evil dwell with thee.*

5   *The foolish shall not stand in thy sight: thou hatest all workers of iniquity.*

6   *Thou shalt destroy them that speak leasing: the LORD will abhor the bloody and deceitful man.*

PSALM 11:5

5   The LORD *trieth the righteous: but the wicked and him that loveth violence his soul hateth.*

JOHN 3:14–17

14   *And as Moses lifted up the serpent in the wilderness, even so must the Son of man be lifted up:*

15   *That whosoever believeth in him should not perish, but have eternal life.*

16   *For God so loved the world, that he gave his only begotten Son, that whosoever believeth in him should not perish, but have everlasting life.*

17   *For God sent not his Son into the world to condemn the world; but that the world through him might be saved.*

A. An unexplainable _____

1 PETER 1:3

3   *Blessed be the God and Father of our Lord Jesus Christ, which according to his abundant mercy…*

LAMENTATIONS 3:22–23

22   *It is of the LORD's mercies that we are not consumed, because his compassions fail not.*

23   *They are new every morning: great is thy faithfulness.*

MICAH 7:18–19

18   *Who is a God like unto thee, that pardoneth iniquity, and passeth by the transgression of the remnant of his heritage? he retaineth not his anger for ever, because he delighteth in mercy.*

19   *He will turn again, he will have compassion upon us; he will subdue our iniquities; and thou wilt cast all their sins into the depths of the sea.*

B. An unequivocal _____

1 PETER 1:3

3 ...hath begotten us again unto a lively hope by the resurrection of Jesus Christ from the dead.

ROMANS 8:32

32 He that spared not his own Son, but delivered him up for us all, how shall he not with him also freely give us all things?

2 CORINTHIANS 9:15

15 Thanks be unto God for his unspeakable gift.

III. A _____ Salvation

JOHN 10:28

28 And I give unto them eternal life; and they shall never perish...

A. Your inheritance is _____ against all enemies.

1 PETER 1:4

4 To an inheritance incorruptible, and undefiled...

ROMANS 8:35–39

35 Who shall separate us from the love of Christ? shall tribulation, or distress, or persecution, or famine, or nakedness, or peril, or sword?

36 As it is written, For thy sake we are killed all the day long; we are accounted as sheep for the slaughter.

37 Nay, in all these things we are more than conquerors through him that loved us.

38 For I am persuaded, that neither death, nor life, nor angels, nor principalities, nor powers, nor things present, nor things to come,

39 Nor height, nor depth, nor any other creature, shall be able to separate us from the love of God, which is in Christ Jesus our Lord.

HEBREWS 13:5

5 Let your conversation be without covetousness: and be content with such things as ye have: for he hath said, I will never leave thee, nor forsake thee.

PSALM 112:7

7 He shall not be afraid of evil tidings: his heart is fixed, trusting in the LORD.

1 PETER 3:13

13 And who is he that will harm you, if ye be followers of that which is good?

B. Your inheritance is _____ for all eternity.

1 PETER 1:4

4 ...and that fadeth not away, reserved in heaven for you.

TITUS 1:2

2 In hope of eternal life, which God, that cannot lie, promised before the world began.

2 CORINTHIANS 4:18

18 While we look not at the things which are seen, but at the things which are not seen: for the things which

are seen are temporal; but the things which are not seen are eternal.

IV. A _____ Salvation

A. *God skillfully keeps His _____.*

1 PETER 1:5

5   *Who are kept by the power of God...*

PSALM 37:28

28   *For the* LORD *loveth judgment, and forsaketh not his saints; they are preserved for ever: but the seed of the wicked shall be cut off.*

2 TIMOTHY 4:18

18   *And the Lord shall deliver me from every evil work, and will preserve me unto his heavenly kingdom: to whom be glory for ever and ever. Amen.*

DEUTERONOMY 33:27

27   *The eternal God is thy refuge, and underneath are the everlasting arms...*

2 TIMOTHY 1:12

12   *...for I know whom I have believed, and am persuaded that he is able to keep that which I have committed unto him against that day.*

B. *God successfully keeps His _____.*

1 PETER 1:5

5   *...through faith unto salvation ready to be revealed in the last time.*

NUMBERS 23:19

19 God is not a man, that he should lie; neither the son of man, that he should repent: hath he said, and shall he not do it? or hath he spoken, and shall he not make it good?

HEBREWS 6:18

18 That by two immutable things, in which it was impossible for God to lie…

2 CORINTHIANS 1:20

20 For all the promises of God in him are yea, and in him Amen, unto the glory of God by us.

Conclusion

_____

_____

_____

Study Questions

1.   Why did Jesus redeem us?

2.   What are some things you can thank God for in your trial?

3.   How do you know that nothing can change what Christ did on the cross?

4.   How can you understand the richness of God's love?

5.   What two things does God give us to carry us through our trials?

6. How can you combat the devil when he tries to frustrate and discourage you during trials?

7. What has God reserved for you after you accept Him?

8. List a verse that affirms our place in Heaven for all eternity.

Memory Verse

2 PETER 3:9

9 The Lord is not slack concerning his promise, as some men count slackness; but is longsuffering to us-ward, not willing that any should perish, but that all should come to repentance.

An Awesome Power

Key Verses

1 Peter 1:5–12

5 *Who are kept by the power of God through faith unto salvation ready to be revealed in the last time.*

6 *Wherein ye greatly rejoice, though now for a season, if need be, ye are in heaviness through manifold temptations:*

7 *That the trial of your faith, being much more precious than of gold that perisheth, though it be tried with fire, might be found unto praise and honour and glory at the appearing of Jesus Christ:*

8 *Whom having not seen, ye love; in whom, though now ye see him not, yet believing, ye rejoice with joy unspeakable and full of glory:*

9 *Receiving the end of your faith, even the salvation of your souls.*

10 *Of which salvation the prophets have inquired and searched diligently, who prophesied of the grace that should come unto you:*

11 *Searching what, or what manner of time the Spirit of Christ which was in them did signify, when it testified beforehand the sufferings of Christ, and the glory that should follow.*

12 *Unto whom it was revealed, that not unto themselves, but unto us they did minister the things, which are now reported unto you by them that have preached the gospel unto you with the Holy Ghost sent down from heaven; which things the angels desire to look into.*

Overview

People's problems are often large because they view our God as small. Until the child of God realizes the scope of God's power, he will live in doubt and fear. God most often shows His power through trials in our lives. It is during these times that the Christian realizes he needs someone bigger than himself.

The exercise that God takes us through in trials refines our faith and makes us stronger. God is not trying to destroy us through the difficulty, but purge and purify us so that His power can flow through us.

Lesson Theme

Often the immediate response of most people when trials come is that God is angry with us. Peter helps us understand that God in His love desires to make us better rather than bitter through the tests of life. Understanding this process will give the student hope in the midst of some of the most difficult circumstances. Some of God's greatest servants have been made in the furnace of affliction.

Revivals are often born in the midst of adverse situations or calamities. In trials, we can rejoice because of God's awesome power.

Introduction

_____

_____

_____

GENESIS 18:14

14 *Is any thing too hard for the LORD?...*

JEREMIAH 32:17

17 *Ah Lord GOD! behold, thou hast made the heaven and the earth by thy great power and stretched out arm, and there is nothing too hard for thee.*

MATTHEW 19:26

26 *But Jesus beheld them, and said unto them, With men this is impossible; but with God all things are possible.*

1 CORINTHIANS 1:25–31

25 *Because the foolishness of God is wiser than men; and the weakness of God is stronger than men.*

26 *For ye see your calling, brethren, how that not many wise men after the flesh, not many mighty, not many noble, are called:*

27 *But God hath chosen the foolish things of the world to confound the wise; and God hath chosen the weak things of the world to confound the things which are mighty;*

28 *And base things of the world, and things which are despised, hath God chosen, yea, and things which are not, to bring to nought things that are:*

29 *That no flesh should glory in his presence.*

30 *But of him are ye in Christ Jesus, who of God is made unto us wisdom, and righteousness, and sanctification, and redemption:*

31 *That, according as it is written, He that glorieth, let him glory in the Lord.*

I. The Possibility of _____ in Trials

A. We are _____ in God's defense.

1 PETER 1:5

5 *Who are kept by the power of God through faith unto salvation ready to be revealed in the last time.*

PROVERBS 3:5–6

5 *Trust in the LORD with all thine heart; and lean not to thine own understanding.*

6 *In all thy ways acknowledge him, and he shall direct thy paths.*

1 CHRONICLES 29:12

12 *Both riches and honour come of thee, and thou reignest over all; and in thine hand is power and might; and in thine hand it is to make great, and to give strength unto all.*

ROMANS 16:25

25 *Now to him that is of power to stablish you…*

PSALM 59:9

9 *Because of his strength will I wait upon thee: for God is my defence.*

B. We are _____ in God's deliverance.

1 PETER 1:6

6   Wherein ye greatly rejoice, though now for a season, if need be, ye are in heaviness through manifold temptations.

PSALM 30:5

5   …weeping may endure for a night, but joy cometh in the morning.

GALATIANS 1:4

4   Who gave himself for our sins, that he might deliver us from this present evil world, according to the will of God and our Father.

2 PETER 2:9

9   The Lord knoweth how to deliver the godly out of temptations…

1 CORINTHIANS 15:55–57

55   O death, where is thy sting? O grave, where is thy victory?

56   The sting of death is sin; and the strength of sin is the law.

57   But thanks be to God, which giveth us the victory through our Lord Jesus Christ.

1 JOHN 3:2–3

2   Beloved, now are we the sons of God, and it doth not yet appear what we shall be: but we know that, when he shall appear, we shall be like him; for we shall see him as he is.

3   And every man that hath this hope in him purifieth himself, even as he is pure.

II. The Purpose of _____ in Trials

JOB 23:10

10 *But he knoweth the way that I take: when he hath tried me, I shall come forth as gold.*

A. The _____ of trials

1 PETER 1:7

7 *That the trial of your faith, being much more precious than of gold that perisheth…*

ISAIAH 48:10

10 *Behold, I have refined thee, but not with silver; I have chosen thee in the furnace of affliction.*

MALACHI 3:3

3 *And he shall sit as a refiner and purifier of silver: and he shall purify the sons of Levi, and purge them as gold and silver, that they may offer unto the* LORD *an offering in righteousness.*

B. The _____ of trials

1 PETER 1:7

7 *…though it be tried with fire…*

JOHN 15:2

2 *Every branch in me that beareth not fruit he taketh away: and every branch that beareth fruit, he purgeth it, that it may bring forth more fruit.*

2 Timothy 2:20–21

20 But in a great house there are not only vessels of gold and of silver, but also of wood and of earth; and some to honour, and some to dishonour.

21 If a man therefore purge himself from these, he shall be a vessel unto honour, sanctified, and meet for the master's use, and prepared unto every good work.

C. The _____ of trials

1 Peter 1:7

7 ...might be found unto praise and honour and glory at the appearing of Jesus Christ.

Philippians 1:20

20 According to my earnest expectation and my hope, that in nothing I shall be ashamed, but that with all boldness, as always, so now also Christ shall be magnified in my body, whether it be by life, or by death.

1 John 2:28

28 And now, little children, abide in him; that, when he shall appear, we may have confidence, and not be ashamed before him at his coming.

III. The Promise of _____ in Trials

Genesis 50:20

20 But as for you, ye thought evil against me; but God meant it unto good, to bring to pass, as it is this day, to save much people alive.

A. A growing _____

1 PETER 1:8

8   *Whom having not seen, ye love; in whom, though now ye see him not, yet believing, ye rejoice with joy unspeakable and full of glory.*

JUDE 21

21   *Keep yourselves in the love of God, looking for the mercy of our Lord Jesus Christ unto eternal life.*

B. A greater _____

1 PETER 1:9

9   *Receiving the end of your faith, even the salvation of your souls.*

REVELATION 21:1–4

1   *And I saw a new heaven and a new earth: for the first heaven and the first earth were passed away; and there was no more sea.*

2   *And I John saw the holy city, new Jerusalem, coming down from God out of heaven, prepared as a bride adorned for her husband.*

3   *And I heard a great voice out of heaven saying, Behold, the tabernacle of God is with men, and he will dwell with them, and they shall be his people, and God himself shall be with them, and be their God.*

4   *And God shall wipe away all tears from their eyes; and there shall be no more death, neither sorrow, nor crying, neither shall there be any more pain: for the former things are passed away.*

IV. The Partnership of _____ in Trials

1 Peter 2:21

21 *For even hereunto were ye called: because Christ also suffered for us, leaving us an example, that ye should follow his steps.*

Hebrews 12:2–3

2 *Looking unto Jesus the author and finisher of our faith; who for the joy that was set before him endured the cross, despising the shame, and is set down at the right hand of God.*

3 *For consider him that endured such contradiction of sinners against himself, lest ye be wearied and faint in your minds.*

A. A prophetic _____

1 Peter 1:10–11

10 *Of which salvation the prophets have inquired and searched diligently, who prophesied of the grace that should come unto you:*

11 *Searching what, or what manner of time the Spirit of Christ which was in them did signify...*

Hebrews 1:1–3

1 *God, who at sundry times and in divers manners spake in time past unto the fathers by the prophets,*

2 *Hath in these last days spoken unto us by his Son, whom he hath appointed heir of all things, by whom also he made the worlds;*

3 *Who being the brightness of his glory, and the express image of his person, and upholding all things by the word*

of his power, when he had by himself purged our sins, sat down on the right hand of the Majesty on high.

B. A profound _____

1 PETER 1:11

11 ...*when it testified beforehand the sufferings of Christ, and the glory that should follow.*

ISAIAH 50:6

6 *I gave my back to the smiters, and my cheeks to them that plucked off the hair: I hid not my face from shame and spitting.*

ISAIAH 53:5

5 *He was wounded for our transgressions, he was bruised for our iniquities: the chastisement of our peace was upon him; and with his stripes we are healed.*

HEBREWS 13:12

12 *Wherefore Jesus also, that he might sanctify the people with his own blood, suffered without the gate.*

LUKE 22:44

44 *And being in an agony he prayed more earnestly; and his sweat was as it were great drops of blood falling down to the ground.*

MARK 15:34

34 *And at the ninth hour Jesus cried with a loud voice, saying, Eloi, Eloi, lama sabachthani? which is, being interpreted, My God, my God, why hast thou forsaken me?*

C. A partnered _____

1 Peter 1:12

12   Unto whom it was revealed, that not unto themselves, but unto us they did minister the things, which are now reported unto you by them that have preached the gospel unto you with the Holy Ghost sent down from heaven; which things the angels desire to look into.

Matthew 16:24

24   Then said Jesus unto his disciples, If any man will come after me, let him deny himself, and take up his cross, and follow me.

Philippians 3:8

8   Yea doubtless, and I count all things but loss for the excellency of the knowledge of Christ Jesus my Lord: for whom I have suffered the loss of all things, and do count them but dung, that I may win Christ.

Conclusion

_____

_____

_____

Study Questions

1. What is always present in the absence of trust?

2. What trials have you not yet trusted God with?

3. What can we always rejoice in no matter our present circumstances?

4. While going through a trial, what is God's purpose?

5. Can you thank God for your trial? Why or why not?

6. What does your trial have the potential to do if you let it?

7. When we are tempted to complain, what should we remember?

8. In what areas of your life has your trial brought you closer to God?

Memory Verse

JOB 23:10

10 But he knoweth the way that I take: when he hath tried me, I shall come forth as gold.

An Admonished Performance

Key Verses

1 PETER 1:13–25

13 Wherefore gird up the loins of your mind, be sober, and hope to the end for the grace that is to be brought unto you at the revelation of Jesus Christ;

14 As obedient children, not fashioning yourselves according to the former lusts in your ignorance:

15 But as he which hath called you is holy, so be ye holy in all manner of conversation;

16 Because it is written, Be ye holy; for I am holy.

17 And if ye call on the Father, who without respect of persons judgeth according to every man's work, pass the time of your sojourning here in fear:

18 Forasmuch as ye know that ye were not redeemed with corruptible things, as silver and gold, from your vain conversation received by tradition from your fathers;

19 But with the precious blood of Christ, as of a lamb without blemish and without spot:

20 Who verily was foreordained before the foundation of the world, but was manifest in these last times for you,

21 Who by him do believe in God, that raised him up from the dead, and gave him glory; that your faith and hope might be in God.

22 Seeing ye have purified your souls in obeying the truth through the Spirit unto unfeigned love of the brethren, see that ye love one another with a pure heart fervently:

23 Being born again, not of corruptible seed, but of incorruptible, by the word of God, which liveth and abideth for ever.

24 For all flesh is as grass, and all the glory of man as the flower of grass. The grass withereth, and the flower thereof falleth away:

25 But the word of the Lord endureth for ever. And this is the word which by the gospel is preached unto you.

Overview

Peter is now going to get down to some application. It is one thing to know something in theory but quite another to practice what you know. God wants us to make our theology a part of our everyday lives. Belief should influence behavior. If it doesn't, then we probably don't really believe what we say we do. God is trying to prepare us, but we must be willing to perform.

Lesson Theme

Several steps are outlined in this chapter that if taken will enable us to put these principles into practice. We can know that God has a plan for our lives including our trials, but we must become doers of what we know. Truth now becomes practical in this lesson as we see how to be performance people because we are principled people.

Introduction

_____

_____

_____

JOHN 13:17

17 If ye know these things, happy are ye if ye do them.

LUKE 6:46

46 And why call ye me, Lord, Lord, and do not the things which I say?

ROMANS 2:21

21 Thou therefore which teachest another, teachest thou not thyself?…

I. Be _____

HEBREWS 12:1

1 Wherefore seeing we also are compassed about with so great a cloud of witnesses, let us lay aside every weight, and the sin which doth so easily beset us, and let us run with patience the race that is set before us.

A. A spiritual _____

1 PETER 1:13

13 Wherefore gird up the loins of your mind…

PROVERBS 23:7

7 For as he thinketh in his heart, so is he…

ROMANS 12:2

2 And be not conformed to this world: but be ye transformed by the renewing of your mind, that ye may prove what is that good, and acceptable, and perfect, will of God.

2 CORINTHIANS 10:5

5   *Casting down imaginations, and every high thing that exalteth itself against the knowledge of God, and bringing into captivity every thought to the obedience of Christ.*

PHILIPPIANS 4:8

8   *Finally, brethren, whatsoever things are true, whatsoever things are honest, whatsoever things are just, whatsoever things are pure, whatsoever things are lovely, whatsoever things are of good report; if there be any virtue, and if there be any praise, think on these things.*

B. A sober _____

1 PETER 1:13

13   *...be sober...*

TITUS 2:12

12   *Teaching us that, denying ungodliness and worldly lusts, we should live soberly, righteously, and godly, in this present world.*

PHILIPPIANS 1:27

27   *Only let your conversation be as it becometh the gospel of Christ...*

1 TIMOTHY 4:12

12   *Let no man despise thy youth; but be thou an example of the believers, in word, in conversation, in charity, in spirit, in faith, in purity.*

C. A surprising _____

1 PETER 1:13

13 ...and hope to the end for the grace that is to brought unto you at the revelation of Jesus Christ.

TITUS 2:13

13 Looking for that blessed hope, and glorious appearing of the great God and our Saviour Jesus Christ.

1 THESSALONIANS 5:1–3

1 But of the times and the seasons, brethren, ye have no need that I write unto you.

2 For yourselves know perfectly that the day of the Lord so cometh as a thief in the night.

3 For when they shall say, Peace and safety; then sudden destruction cometh upon them, as travail upon a woman with child; and they shall not escape.

1 CORINTHIANS 15:51–52

51 Behold, I shew you a mystery; We shall not all sleep, but we shall all be changed,

52 In a moment, in the twinkling of an eye, at the last trump: for the trumpet shall sound, and the dead shall be raised incorruptible, and we shall be changed.

II. Be _____

PROVERBS 4:23

23 Keep thy heart with all diligence; for out of it are the issues of life.

PROVERBS 14:15

15 ...the prudent man looketh well to his going.

A. Reject _____ patterns.

1 PETER 1:14

14 ...not fashioning yourselves according to the former...

EPHESIANS 4:22–24

22 That ye put off concerning the former conversation the old man, which is corrupt according to the deceitful lusts;

23 And be renewed in the spirit of your mind;

24 And that ye put on the new man, which after God is created in righteousness and true holiness.

COLOSSIANS 3:1–3

1 If ye then be risen with Christ, seek those things which are above, where Christ sitteth on the right hand of God.

2 Set your affection on things above, not on things on the earth.

3 For ye are dead, and your life is hid with Christ in God.

PSALM 1:1–2

1 Blessed is the man that walketh not in the counsel of the ungodly, nor standeth in the way of sinners, nor sitteth in the seat of the scornful.

2 But his delight is in the law of the LORD; and in his law doth he meditate day and night.

B. Resist _____ passions.

1 PETER 1:14

14 ...the former lusts in your ignorance.

JAMES 1:14–15

14 But every man is tempted, when he is drawn away of his own lust, and enticed.

15 Then when lust hath conceived, it bringeth forth sin: and sin, when it is finished, bringeth forth death.

2 Timothy 2:22

22   Flee also youthful lusts…

1 Corinthians 6:18–20

18   Flee fornication. Every sin that a man doeth is without the body; but he that committeth fornication sinneth against his own body.

19   What? know ye not that your body is the temple of the Holy Ghost which is in you, which ye have of God, and ye are not your own?

20   For ye are bought with a price: therefore glorify God in your body, and in your spirit, which are God's.

III. Be _____

A. A childlike _____

1 Peter 1:14

14   As obedient children…

1 Samuel 15:22

22   And Samuel said, Hath the Lord as great delight in burnt offerings and sacrifices as in obeying the voice of the Lord? Behold, to obey is better than sacrifice, and to hearken than the fat of rams.

Deuteronomy 5:29

29   Oh that there were such an heart in them, that they would fear me, and keep all my commandments always, that it might be well with them, and with their children for ever.

James 1:25

25   But whoso looketh into the perfect law of liberty, and continueth therein, he being not a forgetful hearer, but a doer of the work, this man shall be blessed in his deed.

B. A Christ-like _____

1 PETER 1:15–16

15   But as he which hath called you is holy, so be ye holy in all manner of conversation;

16   Because it is written, Be ye holy; for I am holy.

LEVITICUS 11:45

45   For I am the LORD that bringeth you up out of the land of Egypt, to be your God: ye shall therefore be holy, for I am holy.

LUKE 1:74–75

74   That he would grant unto us, that we being delivered out of the hand of our enemies might serve him without fear,

75   In holiness and righteousness before him, all the days of our life.

2 CORINTHIANS 7:1

1   Having therefore these promises, dearly beloved, let us cleanse ourselves from all filthiness of the flesh and spirit, perfecting holiness in the fear of God.

IV. Be _____

DEUTERONOMY 33:29

29   Happy art thou, O Israel: who is like unto thee, O people saved by the LORD, the shield of thy help, and who is the sword of thy excellency! and thine enemies shall be found liars unto thee; and thou shalt tread upon their high places.

ROMANS 6:17–18

17   But God be thanked, that ye were the servants of sin, but ye have obeyed from the heart that form of doctrine which was delivered you.

18 Being then made free from sin, ye became the servants of righteousness.

A. Our redemption is not through human _____.

1 Peter 1:17–18

17 And if ye call on the Father, who without respect of persons judgeth according to every man's work, pass the time of your sojourning here in fear:
18 Forasmuch as ye know that ye were not redeemed with corruptible things, as silver and gold, from your vain conversation received by tradition from your fathers.

Matthew 7:22–23

22 Many will say to me in that day, Lord, Lord, have we not prophesied in thy name? and in thy name have cast out devils? and in thy name done many wonderful works?
23 And then will I profess unto them, I never knew you: depart from me, ye that work iniquity.

Romans 3:20

20 Therefore by the deeds of the law there shall no flesh be justified in his sight: for by the law is the knowledge of sin.

Romans 11:6

6 And if by grace, then is it no more of works: otherwise grace is no more grace. But if it be of works, then is it no more grace: otherwise work is no more work.

Romans 10:1–4

1 Brethren, my heart's desire and prayer to God for Israel is, that they might be saved.

2 *For I bear them record that they have a zeal of God, but not according to knowledge.*

3 *For they being ignorant of God's righteousness, and going about to establish their own righteousness, have not submitted themselves unto the righteousness of God.*

4 *For Christ is the end of the law for righteousness to every one that believeth.*

B. Our redemption is through His _____.

1 PETER 1:19–21

19 *But with the precious blood of Christ, as of a lamb without blemish and without spot:*

20 *Who verily was foreordained before the foundation of the world, but was manifest in these last times for you,*

21 *Who by him do believe in God, that raised him up from the dead, and gave him glory; that your faith and hope might be in God.*

HEBREWS 9:22–26

22 *And almost all things are by the law purged with blood; and without shedding of blood is no remission.*

23 *It was therefore necessary that the patterns of things in the heavens should be purified with these; but the heavenly things themselves with better sacrifices than these.*

24 *For Christ is not entered into the holy places made with hands, which are the figures of the true; but into heaven itself, now to appear in the presence of God for us:*

25 *Nor yet that he should offer himself often, as the high priest entereth into the holy place every year with blood of others;*

26 *For then must he often have suffered since the foundation of the world: but now once in the end of the world hath he appeared to put away sin by the sacrifice of himself.*

V. Be _____

PROVERBS 28:21

21 *To have respect of persons is not good...*

A. All are _____ *through the same truth.*
1 PETER 1:22

22 *Seeing ye have purified your souls in obeying the truth through the Spirit...*

JOHN 14:6

6 *Jesus saith unto him, I am the way, the truth, and the life: no man cometh unto the Father, but by me.*

1 TIMOTHY 2:5–6

5 *For there is one God, and one mediator between God and men, the man Christ Jesus;*

6 *Who gave himself a ransom for all, to be testified in due time.*

B. All _____ *the same treatment.*
1 PETER 1:22

22 *...unto unfeigned love of the brethren, see that ye love one another with a pure heart fervently.*

1 JOHN 4:11

11 *Beloved, if God so loved us, we ought also to love one another.*

1 JOHN 4:20–21

20 *If a man say, I love God, and hateth his brother, he is a liar: for he that loveth not his brother whom he hath seen, how can he love God whom he hath not seen?*

21 And this commandment have we from him, That he who loveth God love his brother also.

1 Thessalonians 3:12
12 And the Lord make you to increase and abound in love one toward another, and toward all men, even as we do toward you.

John 15:12
12 This is my commandment, That ye love one another, as I have loved you.

VI. Be _____

A. The _____ *of our message*
1 Peter 1:23
23 Being born again, not of corruptible seed, but of incorruptible, by the word of God, which liveth and abideth for ever.

2 Peter 1:20–21
20 Knowing this first, that no prophecy of the scripture is of any private interpretation.
21 For the prophecy came not in old time by the will of man: but holy men of God spake as they were moved by the Holy Ghost.

Psalm 119:89
89 For ever, O Lord, thy word is settled in heaven.

Psalm 119:152
152 Concerning thy testimonies, I have known of old that thou hast founded them for ever.

PSALM 119:160

160 Thy word is true from the beginning: and every one of thy righteous judgments endureth for ever.

B. The _____ of man

1 PETER 1:24

24 For all flesh is as grass, and all the glory of man as the flower of grass. The grass withereth, and the flower thereof falleth away.

2 CORINTHIANS 3:5

5 Not that we are sufficient of ourselves to think any thing as of ourselves; but our sufficiency is of God.

ROMANS 7:18

18 For I know that in me (that is, in my flesh,) dwelleth no good thing…

JOHN 3:27

27 John answered and said, A man can receive nothing, except it be given him from heaven.

C. The _____ of our mission

1 PETER 1:25

25 But the word of the Lord endureth for ever. And this is the word which by the gospel is preached unto you.

ROMANS 10:13–14

13 For whosoever shall call upon the name of the Lord shall be saved.

14 How then shall they call on him in whom they have not believed? and how shall they believe in him of whom they have not heard? and how shall they hear without a preacher?

LUKE 24:47
47 And that repentance and remission of sins should be preached in his name among all nations, beginning at Jerusalem.

Conclusion

_____

_____

_____

Study Questions

1. What determines how we live?

2. How can a Christian be "girded"?

3. To which emotion does Satan appeal?

4. What is key to winning the battle?

5. How well are you representing Christ to a lost world?

6. To whom have you shown Christ's love recently?

7. What steps are you taking to grow in your Christian walk?

8. What should be our first priority?

Memory Verse

ROMANS 12:2

2 *And be not conformed to this world: but be ye transformed by the renewing of your mind, that ye may prove what is that good, and acceptable, and perfect, will of God.*

An Activated Progress

Key Verses

1 Peter 2:1–8

1   Wherefore laying aside all malice, and all guile, and hypocrisies, and envies, and all evil speakings,

2   As newborn babes, desire the sincere milk of the word, that ye may grow thereby:

3   If so be ye have tasted that the Lord is gracious.

4   To whom coming, as unto a living stone, disallowed indeed of men, but chosen of God, and precious,

5   Ye also, as lively stones, are built up a spiritual house, an holy priesthood, to offer up spiritual sacrifices, acceptable to God by Jesus Christ.

6   Wherefore also it is contained in the scripture, Behold, I lay in Sion a chief corner stone, elect, precious: and he that believeth on him shall not be confounded.

7   Unto you therefore which believe he is precious: but unto them which be disobedient, the stone which the builders disallowed, the same is made the head of the corner,

8   And a stone of stumbling, and a rock of offence, even to them which stumble at the word, being disobedient: whereunto also they were appointed.

Overview

Salvation is a radical change that takes place instantaneously at the moment of personal trust in Christ as our Saviour. Sanctification begins at salvation and is a gradual changing of our lives to become like Christ and does not end until glorification (the moment we enter into the presence of

God in Heaven). This process may be tedious and difficult at times, but it is well worth our commitment to progress. The blessing is ours as we reflect Christ in our attitudes and actions.

Lesson Theme

Change doesn't happen just because we desire or want something better. Salvation requires faith in Christ. Nothing happens until we place our faith in Him for redemption. Sanctification doesn't just happen either. A daily discipline is necessary for a lifetime if we are going to mature into the image of Christ. Peter shares in the opening of chapter 2 the daily process of progress.

Introduction

_____

_____

_____

1 Corinthians 9:24–27

24 Know ye not that they which run in a race run all, but one receiveth the prize? So run, that ye may obtain.

25 And every man that striveth for the mastery is temperate in all things. Now they do it to obtain a corruptible crown; but we an incorruptible.

26 I therefore so run, not as uncertainly; so fight I, not as one that beateth the air:

27 But I keep under my body, and bring it into subjection: lest that by any means, when I have preached to others, I myself should be a castaway.

I. We Must _____ Daily

Genesis 39:10

10 And it came to pass, as she spake to Joseph day by day, that he hearkened not unto her, to lie by her, or to be with her.

1 Corinthians 15:31

31 …I die daily.

A. From injurious _____

1 Peter 2:1

1 Wherefore , laying aside all malice, and all guile…

Romans 12:10

10 Be kindly affectioned one to another with brotherly love; in honour preferring one another.

1 Corinthians 13:4–7

4   *Charity suffereth long, and is kind; charity envieth not; charity vaunteth not itself, is not puffed up,*

5   *Doth not behave itself unseemly, seeketh not her own, is not easily provoked, thinketh no evil;*

6   *Rejoiceth not in iniquity, but rejoiceth in the truth;*

7   *Beareth all things, believeth all things, hopeth all things, endureth all things.*

B. *From an inconsistent* _____

1 Peter 2:1

1   *...and hypocrisies...*

Matthew 23:25–28

25   *Woe unto you, scribes and Pharisees, hypocrites! for ye make clean the outside of the cup and of the platter, but within they are full of extortion and excess.*

26   *Thou blind Pharisee, cleanse first that which is within the cup and platter, that the outside of them may be clean also.*

27   *Woe unto you, scribes and Pharisees, hypocrites! for ye are like unto whited sepulchres, which indeed appear beautiful outward, but are within full of dead men's bones, and of all uncleanness.*

28   *Even so ye also outwardly appear righteous unto men, but within ye are full of hypocrisy and iniquity.*

Titus 1:16

16   *They profess that they know God; but in works they deny him...*

C. *From inflamed* _____

1 Peter 2:1

21   *...and envies...*

1 CORINTHIANS 4:7

7   For who maketh thee to differ from another? and what hast thou that thou didst not receive? now if thou didst receive it, why dost thou glory, as if thou hadst not received it?

PROVERBS 14:30

30   A sound heart is the life of the flesh: but envy the rottenness of the bones.

GALATIANS 5:26

26   Let us not be desirous of vainglory, provoking one another, envying one another.

D. From inappropriate _____

1 PETER 2:1

21   ...and all evil speakings.

MATTHEW 12:34

34   ...for out of the abundance of the heart the mouth speaketh.

1 TIMOTHY 6:3–4

3   If any man teach otherwise, and consent not to wholesome words, even the words of our Lord Jesus Christ, and to the doctrine which is according to godliness.

4   He is proud, knowing nothing...

MATTHEW 12:36–37

36   But I say unto you, That every idle word that men shall speak, they shall give an account thereof in the day of judgment.

37   For by thy words thou shalt be justified, and by thy words thou shalt be condemned.

PSALM 19:14

14 *Let the words of my mouth, and the meditation of my heart, be acceptable in thy sight, O LORD, my strength, and my redeemer.*

PROVERBS 18:21

21 *Death and life are in the power of the tongue...*

II. We Must _____ Daily

JOSHUA 1:8

8 *This book of the law shall not depart out of thy mouth; but thou shalt meditate therein day and night, that thou mayest observe to do according to all that is written therein: for then thou shalt make thy way prosperous, and then thou shalt have good success.*

A. A _____ craving

1 PETER 2:2

2 *As newborn babes, desire the sincere milk of the word, that ye may grow thereby.*

JEREMIAH 15:16

16 *Thy words were found, and I did eat them; and thy word was unto me the joy and rejoicing of mine heart: for I am called by thy name, O LORD God of hosts.*

JOB 23:12

12 *Neither have I gone back from the commandment of his lips; I have esteemed the words of his mouth more than my necessary food.*

PSALM 119:97

97 *O how love I thy law! it is my meditation all the day.*

PSALM 119:72

72   *The law of thy mouth is better unto me than thousands of gold and silver.*

B. A _____ cause

1 PETER 2:3

3   *If so be ye have tasted that the Lord is gracious.*

2 CORINTHIANS 5:15

15   *And that he died for all, that they which live should not henceforth live unto themselves, but unto him which died for them, and rose again.*

1 CORINTHIANS 15:10

10   *But by the grace of God I am what I am: and his grace which was bestowed upon me was not in vain; but I labored more abundantly than they all: yet not I, but the grace of God which was with me.*

III. We Must _____ Daily

A. We are _____ of Christ.

1 PETER 2:5

5   *Ye also, as lively stones, are built up a spiritual house, an holy priesthood, to offer up spiritual sacrifices, acceptable to God by Jesus Christ.*

1 JOHN 4:19

19   *We love him, because he first loved us.*

1 John 3:1–3

1   *Behold, what manner of love the Father hath bestowed upon us, that we should be called the sons of God: therefore the world knoweth us not, because it knew him not.*

2   *Beloved, now are we the sons of God, and it doth not yet appear what we shall be: but we know that, when he shall appear, we shall be like him; for we shall see him as he is.*

3   *And every man that hath this hope in him purifieth himself, even as he is pure.*

B. We are _____ through the church.

1 Peter 2:6–7

6   *Wherefore also it is contained in the scripture, Behold, I lay in Sion a chief corner stone, elect, precious: and he that believeth on him shall not be confounded.*

7   *Unto you therefore which believe he is precious: but unto them which be disobedient, the stone which the builders disallowed, the same is made the head of the corner.*

Ephesians 5:25

25   *Husbands, love your wives, even as Christ also loved the church, and gave himself for it.*

Colossians 1:17–18

17   *And he is before all things, and by him all things consist.*

18   *And he is the head of the body, the church...*

Hebrews 10:22–25

22   *Let us draw near with a true heart in full assurance of faith, having our hearts sprinkled from an evil conscience, and our bodies washed with pure water.*

23 Let us hold fast the profession of our faith without wavering; (for he is faithful that promised;)
24 And let us consider one another to provoke unto love and to good works:
25 Not forsaking the assembling of ourselves together, as the manner of some is; but exhorting one another: and so much the more, as ye see the day approaching.

1 TIMOTHY 3:15

15 But if I tarry long, that thou mayest know how thou oughtest to behave thyself in the house of God, which is the church of the living God, the pillar and ground of the truth.

C. We are in a _____ with the contentious.

1 PETER 2:8

8 And a stone of stumbling, and a rock of offence, even to them which stumble at the word, being disobedient: whereunto also they were appointed.

MATTHEW 24:9

9 ...and ye shall be hated of all nations for my name's sake.

LUKE 6:22

22 Blessed are ye, when men shall hate you, and when they shall separate you from their company, and shall reproach you, and cast out your name as evil, for the Son of man's sake.

JOHN 17:14

14 I have given them thy word; and the world hath hated them, because they are not of the world, even as I am not of the world.

1 JOHN 3:13

13   *Marvel not, my brethren, if the world hate you.*

Conclusion

_____

_____

_____

Study Questions

1. What is sanctification?

2. How can you be prepared for the inevitable battles against the enemy?

3. Is there something not right between you and another Christian? What can you do today to make it right?

4. What is the leading excuse for people not getting saved?

5. What do our words reveal?

6. How are you daily loving the Lord?

7. Why did God establish the church?

8. What steps can you take to grow in your walk with God?

Memory Verse

PSALM 19:14

14 Let the words of my mouth, and the meditation of my heart, be acceptable in thy sight, O LORD, my strength and my redeemer.

An Accepted Purging

Key Verses

1 PETER 2:9–12

9   But ye are a chosen generation, a royal priesthood, an holy nation, a peculiar people; that ye should shew forth the praises of him who hath called you out of darkness into his marvellous light:

10   Which in time past were not a people, but are now the people of God: which had not obtained mercy, but now have obtained mercy.

11   Dearly beloved, I beseech you as strangers and pilgrims, abstain from fleshly lusts, which war against the soul;

12   Having your conversation honest among the Gentiles: that, whereas they speak against you as evildoers, they may by your good works, which they shall behold, glorify God in the day of visitation.

Overview

God wants fellowship with His creation. Sin separated us from God, and it is only through the finished work of Christ on the cross that we can be reconciled to Him. Ultimately, God will take us to Heaven where we will live with Him forever. For the time being He has left us here in this world to reach others with the message of salvation. However, while here He does not want us to become like the world. We are *in* the world but not to be *of* the world.

Lesson Theme

We are new creatures in Christ and as a result are different from those in this world who are not born again. The danger is that the rotten can easily spoil the good. God is aware that His people can easily become just like the world. In this portion of 1 Peter, God reminds His children who they are and why they are to live differently than those who are not His children. A farmer who works out in a dusty field all day needs a bath before his wife and family want much to do with him. Likewise, God's people need a daily purging from the world to have fellowship with their Father.

Introduction

_____

_____

_____

1 John 2:15–17

15 Love not the world, neither the things that are in the world. If any man love the world, the love of the Father is not in him.

16 For all that is in the world, the lust of the flesh, and the lust of the eyes, and the pride of life, is not of the Father, but is of the world.

17 And the world passeth away, and the lust thereof: but he that doeth the will of God abideth for ever.

Colossians 3:2

2 Set your affection on things above, not on things on the earth.

James 4:4

4 Ye adulterers and adulteresses, know ye not that the friendship of the world is enemity with God? whosoever therefore will be a friend of the world is the enemy of God.

I. Our _____

Romans 10:1–10

1 Brethren, my heart's desire and prayer to God for Israel is, that they might be saved.

2 For I bear them record that they have a zeal of God, but not according to knowledge.

3 For they being ignorant of God's righteousness, and going about to establish their own righteousness, have not submitted themselves unto the righteousness of God.

4   For Christ is the end of the law for righteousness to every one that believeth.

5   For Moses describeth the righteousness which is of the law, That the man which doeth those things shall live by them.

6   But the righteousness which is of faith speaketh on this wise, Say not in thine heart, Who shall ascend into heaven? (that is, to bring Christ down from above:)

7   Or, Who shall descend into the deep? (that is, to bring up Christ again from the dead.)

8   But what saith it? The word is nigh thee, even in thy mouth, and in thy heart: that is, the word of faith, which we preach;

9   That if thou shalt confess with thy mouth the Lord Jesus, and shalt believe in thine heart that God hath raised him from the dead, thou shalt be saved.

10   For with the heart man believeth unto righteousness; and with the mouth confession is made unto salvation.

A. We are _____.

1 PETER 2:9

9   But ye are a chosen generation…

JOHN 1:12

12   But as many as received him, to them gave he power to become the sons of God, even to them that believe on his name.

GALATIANS 4:7

7   Wherefore thou art no more a servant, but a son; and if a son, then an heir of God through Christ.

B. We are a _____.

1 PETER 2:9

9   …a royal priesthood…

HEBREWS 4:16

16 *Let us therefore come boldly unto the throne of grace, that we may obtain mercy, and find grace to help in time of need.*

ISAIAH 65:24

24 *And it shall come to pass, that before they call, I will answer; and while they are yet speaking, I will hear.*

1 JOHN 5:14–15

14 *And this is the confidence that we have in him, that, if we ask any thing according to his will, he heareth us:*

15 *And if we know that he hear us, whatsoever we ask, we know that we have the petitions that we desired of him.*

C. We are _____.

1 PETER 2:9

9 *...an holy nation...*

PHILIPPIANS 2:15

15 *That ye may be blameless and harmless, the sons of God, without rebuke, in the midst of a crooked and perverse nation, among whom ye shine as lights in the world.*

1 THESSALONIANS 3:13

13 *To the end he may stablish your hearts unblameable in holiness before God, even our Father, at the coming of our Lord Jesus Christ with all his saints.*

1 THESSALONIANS 5:23

23 *And the very God of peace sanctify you wholly; and I pray God your whole spirit and soul and body be preserved blameless unto the coming of our Lord Jesus Christ.*

D. We are _____.

1 PETER 2:9

9 *...a peculiar people...*

PSALM 101:2–7

2 *I will behave myself wisely in a perfect way. O when wilt thou come unto me? I will walk within my house with a perfect heart.*

3 *I will set no wicked thing before mine eyes: I hate the work of them that turn aside; it shall not cleave to me.*

4 *A froward heart shall depart from me: I will not know a wicked person.*

5 *Whoso privily slandereth his neighbour, him will I cut off: him that hath an high look and a proud heart will not I suffer.*

6 *Mine eyes shall be upon the faithful of the land, that they may dwell with me: he that walketh in a perfect way, he shall serve me.*

7 *He that worketh deceit shall not dwell within my house: he that telleth lies shall not tarry in my sight.*

1 JOHN 2:6

6 *He that saith he abideth in him ought himself also so to walk, even as he walked.*

EPHESIANS 5:15

15 *See then that ye walk circumspectly, not as fools, but as wise.*

II. Our _____

1 CORINTHIANS 10:31

31 *Whether therefore ye eat, or drink, or whatsoever ye do, do all to the glory of God.*

2 CORINTHIANS 4:5

5 *For we preach not ourselves, but Christ Jesus the Lord; and ourselves your servants for Jesus' sake.*

A. To magnify the _____

1 PETER 2:9

9 *…that ye should shew the praises of him…*

ROMANS 15:6

6 *That ye may with one mind and one mouth glorify God, even the Father of our Lord Jesus Christ.*

1 CORINTHIANS 6:20

20 *For ye are bought with a price: therefore glorify God in your body, and in your spirit, which are God's.*

B. To make a _____

1 PETER 2:9

9 *…who hath called you out of darkness into his marvellous light:*

MATTHEW 5:14–16

14 *Ye are the light of the world. A city that is set on a hill cannot be hid.*

15 *Neither do men light a candle, and put it under a bushel, but on a candlestick; and it giveth light unto all that are in the house.*

16 *Let your light so shine before men, that they may see your good works, and glorify your Father which is in heaven.*

III. Our _____

EPHESIANS 2:1–3

1   And you hath he quickened, who were dead in trespasses and sins;

2   Wherein in time past ye walked according to the course of this world, according to the prince of the power of the air, the spirit that now worketh in the children of disobedience:

3   Among whom also we all had our conversation in times past in the lusts of our flesh, fulfilling the desires of the flesh and of the mind; and were by nature the children of wrath, even as others.

A. Once a _____—now a _____

1 PETER 2:10

10   Which in time past were not a people, but are now the people of God...

2 CORINTHIANS 5:17

17   Therefore if any man be in Christ, he is a new creature: old things are passed away; behold, all things are become new.

JAMES 5:19–20

19   Brethren, if any of you do err from the truth, and one convert him;

20   Let him know, that he which converteth the sinner from the error of his way shall save a soul from death, and shall hide a multitude of sins.

B. Once under _____—now _____

1 PETER 2:10

10   ...which had not obtained mercy, but now have obtained mercy.

PSALM 103:12

12   As far as the east is from the west, so far hath he removed our transgressions from us.

ACTS 13:39

39   And by him all that believe are justified from all things, from which ye could not be justified by the law of Moses.

ROMANS 5:1

1   Therefore being justified by faith, we have peace with God through our Lord Jesus Christ.

1 CORINTHIANS 6:11

11   And such were some of you: but ye are washed, but ye are sanctified, but ye are justified in the name of the Lord Jesus, and by the Spirit of our God.

GALATIANS 3:24

24   Wherefore the law was our schoolmaster to bring us unto Christ, that we might be justified by faith.

IV. Our _____

2 PETER 3:17

17   Ye therefore, beloved, seeing ye know these things before, beware lest ye also, being led away with the error of the wicked, fall from your own steadfastness.

A. A compassionate _____

1 PETER 2:11

11   Dearly beloved…

JEREMIAH 31:3

3   *The* LORD *hath appeared of old unto me, saying, Yea, I have loved thee with an everlasting love: therefore with lovingkindness have I drawn thee.*

HEBREWS 12:5–6

5   *And ye have forgotten the exhortation which speaketh unto you as unto children, My son, despise not thou the chastening of the Lord, nor faint when thou art rebuked of him:*

6   *For whom the Lord loveth he chasteneth, and scourgeth every son whom he receiveth.*

B. A clear _____

1 PETER 2:11

11   *…I beseech you as strangers and pilgrims, abstain from fleshly lusts, which war against the soul.*

EPHESIANS 5:11–12

11   *And have no fellowship with the unfruitful works of darkness, but rather reprove them.*

12   *For it is a shame even to speak of those things which are done of them in secret.*

PROVERBS 1:10

10   *My son, if sinners entice thee, consent thou not.*

HEBREWS 11:24–26

24   *By faith Moses, when he was come to years, refused to be called the son of Pharaoh's daughter;*

25   *Choosing rather to suffer affliction with the people of God, than to enjoy the pleasures of sin for a season;*

26 Esteeming the reproach of Christ greater riches than the treasures in Egypt: for he had respect unto the recompence of the reward.

C. A conversation _____

1 PETER 2:12

12 Having your conversation honest among the Gentiles...

DANIEL 6:3–4

3 Then this Daniel was preferred above the presidents and princes, because an excellent spirit was in him; and the king thought to set him over the whole realm.

4 Then the presidents and princes sought to find occasion against Daniel concerning the kingdom; but they could find none occasion nor fault; forasmuch as he was faithful, neither was there any error or fault found in him.

D. A common _____

1 PETER 2:12

12 ...that, whereas they speak against you as evildoers...

DANIEL 6:5–7

5 Then said these men, We shall not find any occasion against this Daniel, except we find it against him concerning the law of his God.

6 Then these presidents and princes assembled together to the king, and said thus unto him, King Darius, live for ever.

7 All the presidents of the kingdom, the governors, and the princes, the counsellors, and the captains, have consulted together to establish a royal statute, and to make a firm decree, that whosoever shall ask a petition of

any God or man for thirty days, save of thee, O king, he shall be cast into the den of lions.

PSALM 119:110

110 The wicked have laid snares for me: yet I erred not from thy precepts.

V. Our _____

1 SAMUEL 30:6

6 And David was greatly distressed; for the people spake of stoning him, because the soul of all the people was grieved, every man for his sons and for his daughters: but David encouraged himself in the LORD his God.

A. A _____ *light*

1 PETER 2:12

12 ...they may by your good works, which they shall behold...

PSALM 51:2, 7

2 Wash me thoroughly from mine iniquity, and cleanse me from my sin.

7 Purge me with hyssop, and I shall be clean: wash me, and I shall be whiter than snow.

PSALM 79:9

9 Help us, O God of our salvation, for the glory of thy name: and deliver us, and purge away our sins, for thy name's sake.

B. A _____ *life*

1 PETER 2:12

12   *...glorify God in the day of visitation.*

MARK 5:14–15

14   *And they that fed the swine fled, and told it in the city, and in the country. And they went out to see what it was that was done.*

15   *And they come to Jesus, and see him that was possessed with the devil, and had the legion, sitting, and clothed, and in his right mind: and they were afraid.*

JOHN 9:24–25

24   *Then again called they the man that was blind, and said unto him, Give God the praise: we know that this man is a sinner.*

25   *He answered and said, Whether he be a sinner or no, I know not: one thing I know, that, whereas I was blind, now I see.*

Conclusion

_____

_____

_____

Study Questions

1. In whom is our position of righteousness found?

2. Why do we have unrestrained access to God?

3. What does being blameless mean?

4. What can you do this week to make an impact on someone's life?

5. Through what process have our sins been removed?

6. What motivates everything God asks us to do?

7. Why do we need to stay vigilant at all times?

8. How can you keep your light clean and ready for God to use?

Memory Verse

HEBREWS 4:16

16 Let us therefore come boldly unto the throne of grace, that we may obtain mercy, and find grace to help in time of need.

An Amiable Pursuit

Text

1 PETER 2:13–25

13   *Submit yourselves to every ordinance of man for the Lord's sake: whether it be to the king, as supreme;*

14   *Or unto governors, as unto them that are sent by him for the punishment of evildoers, and for the praise of them that do well.*

15   *For so is the will of God, that with well doing ye may put to silence the ignorance of foolish men:*

16   *As free, and not using your liberty for a cloke of maliciousness, but as the servants of God.*

17   *Honour all men. Love the brotherhood. Fear God. Honour the king.*

18   *Servants, be subject to your masters with all fear; not only to the good and gentle, but also to the froward.*

19   *For this is thankworthy, if a man for conscience toward God endure grief, suffering wrongfully.*

20   *For what glory is it, if, when ye be buffeted for your faults, ye shall take it patiently? but if, when ye do well, and suffer for it, ye take it patiently, this is acceptable with God.*

21   *For even hereunto were ye called: because Christ also suffered for us, leaving us an example, that ye should follow his steps:*

22   *Who did no sin, neither was guile found in his mouth:*

23   *Who, when he was reviled, reviled not again; when he suffered, he threatened not; but committed himself to him that judgeth righteously:*

24 *Who his own self bare our sins in his own body on the tree, that we, being dead to sins, should live unto righteousness: by whose stripes ye were healed.*

25 *For ye were as sheep going astray; but are now returned unto the Shepherd and Bishop of your souls.*

Overview

The focus in this text is now on how this change on the inside of us is going to affect how we live on the outside. Our responsibilities, our relationships, and our reactions are all going to be different because what fuels us from the inside out is the Spirit of God who is now in control. Yielding to the Spirit rather than our flesh will give us unlimited opportunities to propagate our faith as God commands.

Lesson Theme

This passage covers three very important areas of our lives as Christians—those over us, those around us, and those against us. Our testimonies are at stake in each of these vital relationships. Peter himself struggled in these areas early on in his life and now gives good advice from what he has learned.

Introduction

_____

_____

_____

PROVERBS 16:9

9 *A man's heart deviseth his way: but the* LORD *directeth his steps.*

PSALM 37:23–25, 31

23 *The steps of a good man are ordered by the* LORD: *and he delighteth in his way.*

24 *Though he fall, he shall not be utterly cast down: for the* LORD *upholdeth him with his hand.*

25 *I have been young, and now am old; yet have I not seen the righteous forsaken, nor his seed begging bread.*

31 *The law of his God is in his heart; none of his steps shall slide.*

COLOSSIANS 4:12

12 *…that ye may stand perfect and complete in all the will of God.*

I. Our Responsibility to _____

A. *A patriotic allegiance toward* _____

1 PETER 2:13–14

13 *Submit yourselves to every ordinance of man for the Lord's sake: whether it be to the king, as supreme;*

14 *Or unto governors, as unto them that are sent by him for the punishment of evildoers, and for the praise of them that do well.*

Romans 13:1–7

1   Let every soul be subject unto the higher powers. For there is no power but of God: the powers that be are ordained of God.

2   Whosoever therefore resisteth the power, resisteth the ordinance of God: and they that resist shall receive to themselves damnation.

3   For rulers are not a terror to good works, but to the evil. Wilt thou then not be afraid of the power? do that which is good, and thou shalt have praise of the same:

4   For he is the minister of God to thee for good. But if thou do that which is evil, be afraid; for he beareth not the sword in vain: for he is the minister of God, a revenger to execute wrath upon him that doeth evil.

5   Wherefore ye must needs be subject, not only for wrath, but also for conscience sake.

6   For for this cause pay ye tribute also: for they are God's ministers, attending continually upon this very thing.

7   Render therefore to all their dues: tribute to whom tribute is due; custom to whom custom; fear to whom fear; honour to whom honour.

B. A positive attitude toward the _____

1 Peter 2:15

15   For so is the will of God, that with well doing ye may put to silence the ignorance of foolish men.

Proverbs 25:21–22

21   If thine enemy be hungry, give him bread to eat; and if he be thirsty, give him water to drink:

22   For thou shalt heap coals of fire upon his head, and the Lord shall reward thee.

MATTHEW 5:44

44 But I say unto you, Love your enemies, bless them that curse you, do good to them that hate you, and pray for them which despitefully use you, and persecute you.

1 THESSALONIANS 5:15

15 See that none render evil for evil unto any man; but ever follow that which is good, both among yourselves, and to all men.

C. A parallel application toward _____

1 PETER 2:16

16 As free, and not using your liberty for a cloke of maliciousness, but as the servants of God.

ISAIAH 1:19–20

19 If ye be willing and obedient, ye shall eat the good of the land:
20 But if ye refuse and rebel, ye shall be devoured with the sword: for the mouth of the LORD hath spoken it.

DEUTERONOMY 30:19

19 I call heaven and earth to record this day against you, that I have set before you life and death, blessing and cursing: therefore choose life, that both thou and thy seed may live.

II. Our Relationship in _____

ACTS 17:26

26 And hath made of one blood all nations of men for to dwell on all the face of the earth...

A. _____ all.

1 PETER 2:17

17   Honour all men...

JOHN 3:16

16   For God so loved the world...

EXODUS 20:13

13   Thou shalt not kill.

GENESIS 9:6

6   Whoso sheddeth man's blood, by man shall his blood be shed: for in the image of God made he man.

B. _____ in assembly.

1 PETER 2:17

17   ...Love the brotherhood...

GALATIANS 6:10

10   As we have therefore opportunity, let us do good unto all men, especially unto them who are of the household of faith.

ROMANS 12:13

13   Distributing to the necessity of saints; given to hospitality.

ACTS 20:35

35   I have shewed you all things, how that so laboring ye ought to support the weak, and to remember the words of the Lord Jesus, how he said, It is more blessed to give than to receive.

Hebrews 6:10

10   For God is not unrighteous to forget your work and labour of love, which ye have shewed toward his name, in that ye have ministered to the saints, and do minister.

C. _____ *the Almighty.*

1 Peter 2:17

17   …Fear God…

Colossians 1:16–19

16   For by him were all things created, that are in heaven, and that are in earth, visible and invisible, whether they be thrones, or dominions, or principalities, or powers: all things were created by him, and for him:

17   And he is before all things, and by him all things consist.

18   And he is the head of the body, the church: who is the beginning, the firstborn from the dead; that in all things he might have the preeminence.

19   For it hath pleased the Father that in him should all fulness dwell.

Matthew 6:33

33   But seek ye first the kingdom of God, and his righteousness; and all these things shall be added unto you.

Proverbs 16:7

7   When a man's ways please the Lord, he maketh even his enemies to be at peace with him.

D. _____ *authority.*

1 Peter 2:17–18

17   …Honour the king.

18   Servants, be subject to your masters with all fear…

EPHESIANS 6:5–8

5   Servants, be obedient to them that are your masters according to the flesh, with fear and trembling, in singleness of your heart, as unto Christ.

6   Not with eyeservice, as menpleasers; but as the servants of Christ, doing the will of God from the heart.

7   With good will doing service, as to the Lord, and not to men:

8   Knowing that whatsoever good thing any man doeth, the same shall he receive of the Lord, whether he be bond or free.

1 TIMOTHY 6:1

1   Let as many servants as are under the yoke count their own masters worthy of all honour, that the name of God and his doctrine be not blasphemed.

III. Our Reaction to _____

PROVERBS 24:10

10   If thou faint in the day of adversity, thy strength is small.

A. An irritable _____

1 PETER 2:19–20

19   For this is thankworthy, if a man for conscience toward God endure grief, suffering wrongfully.

20   For what glory is it, if, when ye be buffeted for your faults, ye shall take it patiently? but if, when ye do well, and suffer for it, ye take it patiently, this is acceptable with God.

LUKE 6:27–35

27 But I say unto you which hear, Love your enemies, do good to them which hate you,

28 Bless them that curse you, and pray for them which despitefully use you.

29 And unto him that smiteth thee on the one cheek offer also the other; and him that taketh away thy cloke forbid not to take thy coat also.

30 Give to every man that asketh of thee; and of him that taketh away thy goods ask them not again.

31 And as ye would that men should do to you, do ye also to them likewise.

32 For if ye love them which love you, what thank have ye? for sinners also love those that love them.

33 And if ye do good to them which do good to you, what thank have ye? for sinners also do even the same.

34 And if ye lend to them of whom ye hope to receive, what thank have ye? for sinners also lend to sinners, to receive as much again.

35 But love ye your enemies, and do good, and lend, hoping for nothing again; and your reward shall be great, and ye shall be the children of the Highest: for he is kind unto the unthankful and to the evil.

B. An incredible _____

1 PETER 2:21–25

21 For even hereunto were ye called: because Christ also suffered for us, leaving us an example, that ye should follow his steps:

22 Who did no sin, neither was guile found in his mouth:

23 Who, when he was reviled, reviled not again; when he suffered, he threatened not; but committed himself to him that judgeth righteously:

24 *Who his own self bare our sins in his own body on the tree, that we, being dead to sins, should live unto righteousness: by whose stripes ye were healed.*

25 *For ye were as sheep going astray; but are now returned unto the Shepherd and Bishop of your souls.*

Isaiah 53:7

7 *He was oppressed, and he was afflicted, yet he opened not his mouth: he is brought as a lamb to the slaughter, and as a sheep before her shearers is dumb, so he openeth not his mouth.*

Matthew 11:29

29 *Take my yoke upon you, and learn of me; for I am meek and lowly in heart: and ye shall find rest unto your souls.*

Conclusion

_____

_____

_____

Proverbs 3:5–6

5 *Trust in the Lord with all thine heart; and lean not unto thine own understanding.*

6 *In all thy ways acknowledge him, and he shall direct thy paths.*

Study Questions

1. When do our lives have the greatest impact?

2. Why are we to treat everyone with proper respect and kindness?

3. In order for us to have healthy horizontal relationships, what relationship needs to be right?

4. How can we show the love of Christ to our fellow believers?

5. What is the purpose for God-appointed authorities in our lives?

6. Is there an authority in your life to whom you are struggling to submit?

7. Whose life should you look to for a proper reaction to trials?

8. Write out a verse that will help you remember to forgive others when they mistreat you.

Memory Verse

JOHN 13:35
35 By this shall all men know that ye are my disciples, if ye have love one to another.

An Affectionate Patience

Text

1 Peter 3:1–12

1   Likewise, ye wives, be in subjection to your own husbands; that, if any obey not the word, they also may without the word be won by the conversation of the wives;

2   While they behold your chaste conversation coupled with fear.

3   Whose adorning let it not be that outward adorning of plaiting the hair, and of wearing of gold, or of putting on of apparel;

4   But let it be the hidden man of the heart, in that which is not corruptible, even the ornament of a meek and quiet spirit, which is in the sight of God of great price.

5   For after this manner in the old time the holy women also, who trusted in God, adorned themselves, being in subjection unto their own husbands:

6   Even as Sara obeyed Abraham, calling him lord: whose daughters ye are, as long as ye do well, and are not afraid with any amazement.

7   Likewise, ye husbands, dwell with them according to knowledge, giving honour unto the wife, as unto the weaker vessel, and as being heirs together of the grace of life; that your prayers be not hindered.

8   Finally, be ye all of one mind, having compassion one of another, love as brethren, be pitiful, be courteous:

9   Not rendering evil for evil, or railing for railing: but contrariwise blessing; knowing that ye are thereunto called, that ye should inherit a blessing.

10   For he that will love life, and see good days, let him refrain his tongue from evil, and his lips that they speak no guile:

11   Let him eschew evil, and do good; let him seek peace, and ensue it.

12   For the eyes of the Lord are over the righteous, and his ears are open unto their prayers: but the face of the Lord is against them that do evil.

Overview

The most noticeable and important attribute that God possesses from our perspective is His love. It is this attribute that attracts us to Him. We wouldn't know anything about love apart from God, for He is love (1 John 4:8). The agape unconditional love that God has toward us is to be emulated in our lives and is only possible with His help. What a powerful testimony we possess when we demonstrate the love of God.

Lesson Theme

You can't love in the abstract. We often talk about love and define it carefully, but love always has an object. It's tangible. If God had merely loved—our lives wouldn't be any different. But God so loved—that He gave. God commendeth His love toward us—He proved it by sending His Son to this world. Lots of people today talk about love, but it's merely a theory. Chapter 3 of Peter's epistle puts the theory into practice in a tangible way.

Introduction

_____

_____

_____

1 Corinthians 13:13

13 And now abideth faith, hope, charity, these three; but the greatest of these is charity.

John 13:35

35 By this shall all men know that ye are my disciples, if ye have love one to another.

1 John 3:14

14 We know that we have passed from death to unto life, because we love the brethren. He that loveth not his brother abideth in death.

I.   An Honorable _____

Ephesians 5:21–6:4

21 Submitting yourselves one to another in the fear of God.

22 Wives, submit yourselves unto your own husbands, as unto the Lord.

23 For the husband is the head of the wife, even as Christ is the head of the church: and he is the saviour of the body.

24 Therefore as the church is subject unto Christ, so let the wives be to their own husbands in every thing.

25 Husbands, love your wives, even as Christ also loved the church, and gave himself for it;

26 That he might sanctify and cleanse it with the washing of water by the word,

27 *That he might present it to himself a glorious church, not having spot, or wrinkle, or any such thing; but that it should be holy and without blemish.*

28 *So ought men to love their wives as their own bodies. He that loveth his wife loveth himself.*

29 *For no man ever yet hated his own flesh; but nourisheth and cherisheth it, even as the Lord the church:*

30 *For we are members of his body, of his flesh, and of his bones.*

31 *For this cause shall a man leave his father and mother, and shall be joined unto his wife, and they two shall be one flesh.*

32 *This is a great mystery: but I speak concerning Christ and the church.*

33 *Nevertheless let every one of you in particular so love his wife even as himself; and the wife see that she reverence her husband.*

1 *Children, obey your parents in the Lord: for this is right.*

2 *Honour thy father and mother; (which is the first commandment with promise;)*

3 *That it may be well with thee, and thou mayest live long on the earth.*

4 *And, ye fathers, provoke not your children to wrath: but bring them up in the nurture and admonition of the Lord.*

A. A submissive _____

1 Peter 3:1

1 *Likewise, ye wives, be in subjection to your own husbands…*

Genesis 2:18

18 *And the Lord God said, It is not good that the man should be alone; I will make him an help meet for him.*

PROVERBS 18:22

22 *Whoso findeth a wife findeth a good thing, and obtaineth favour of the* LORD.

PROVERBS 12:4

4 *A virtuous woman is a crown to her husband: but she that maketh ashamed is as rottenness in his bones.*

PROVERBS 31:10

10 *Who can find a virtuous woman? for her price is far above rubies.*

B. A sovereign _____

1 PETER 3:1–2

1 *...that, if any obey not the word, they also may without the word be won by the conversation of the wives;*
2 *While they behold your chaste conversation coupled with fear.*

PSALM 27:10

10 *When my father and my mother forsake me, then the* LORD *will take me up.*

PROVERBS 29:25

25 *The fear of man bringeth a snare: but whoso putteth his trust in the* LORD *shall be safe.*

1 THESSALONIANS 1:8

8 *For from you sounded out the word of the Lord not only in Macedonia and Achaia, but also in every place your faith to God-ward is spread abroad; so that we need not to speak any thing.*

HEBREWS 11:4

4   *By faith Abel offered unto God a more excellent sacrifice than Cain, by which he obtained witness that he was righteous, God testifying of his gifts: and by it he being dead yet speaketh.*

C. A sterling _____

1 PETER 3:3–6

3   *Whose adorning let it not be that outward adorning of plaiting the hair, and of wearing of gold, or of putting on of apparel;*

4   *But let it be the hidden man of the heart, in that which is not corruptible, even the ornament of a meek and quiet spirit, which is in the sight of God of great price.*

5   *For after this manner in the old time the holy women also, who trusted in God, adorned themselves, being in subjection unto their own husbands:*

6   *Even as Sara obeyed Abraham, calling him lord: whose daughters ye are, as long as ye do well, and are not afraid with any amazement.*

PSALM 26:3

3   *…I have walked in thy truth.*

PSALM 86:11

11   *Teach me thy way, O LORD; I will walk in thy truth: unite my heart to fear thy name.*

2 JOHN 4

4   *I rejoiced greatly that I found of thy children walking in truth, as we have received a commandment from the Father.*

3 JOHN 4

4   *I have no greater joy than to hear that my children walk in truth.*

GENESIS 5:24

24   *And Enoch walked with God…*

D. A sensational _____

1 PETER 3:7

7   *Likewise, ye husbands, dwell with them according to knowledge, giving honour unto the wife, as unto the weaker vessel, and as being heirs together of the grace of life; that your prayers be not hindered.*

GENESIS 2:23–24

23   *And Adam said, This is now bone of my bones, and flesh of my flesh: she shall be called Woman, because she was taken out of the man.*

24   *Therefore shall a man leave his father and his mother, and shall cleave unto his wife: and they shall be one flesh.*

PROVERBS 5:18

18   *Let thy fountain be blessed: and rejoice with the wife of thy youth.*

EPHESIANS 5:25

25   *Husbands, love your wives, even as Christ also loved the church, and gave himself for it.*

II. A Harmonious _____

A. _____ *a reconciling spirit.*

1 PETER 3:8–9

8 *Finally, be ye all of one mind, having compassion one of another, love as brethren, be pitiful, be courteous.*

9 *Not rendering evil for evil, or railing for railing: but contrariwise blessing; knowing that ye are thereunto called, that ye should inherit a blessing.*

LEVITICUS 19:18

18 *Thou shalt not avenge, nor bear any grudge against the children of thy people, but thou shalt love thy neighbour as thyself: I am the LORD.*

PROVERBS 24:29

29 *Say not, I will do so to him as he hath done to me: I will render to the man according to his work.*

ROMANS 12:17

17 *Recompense to no man evil for evil. Provide things honest in the sight of all men.*

B. _____ *a ruinous speech.*

1 PETER 3:10

10 *For he that will love life, and see good days, let him refrain his tongue from evil, and his lips that they speak no guile.*

PSALM 34:13

13 *Keep thy tongue from evil, and thy lips from speaking guile.*

PROVERBS 13:3

3 *He that keepeth his mouth keepeth his life: but he that openeth wide his lips shall have destruction.*

TITUS 3:2

2 *To speak evil of no man, to be no brawlers, but gentle, shewing all meekness unto all men.*

EPHESIANS 4:31

31 *Let all bitterness, and wrath, and anger, and clamour, and evil speaking, be away from you, with all malice.*

JAMES 4:11

11 *Speak not evil one of another, brethren. He that speaketh evil of his brother, and judgeth his brother, speaketh evil of the law, and judgeth the law: but if thou judge the law, thou art not a doer of the law, but a judge.*

C. _____ *a repulsive sin.*

1 PETER 3:11

11 *Let him eschew evil, and do good; let him seek peace, and ensue it.*

PSALM 37:27

27 *Depart from evil, and do good…*

PSALM 34:14

14 *Depart from evil, and do good; seek peace, and pursue it.*

1 CORINTHIANS 15:34

34 *Awake to righteousness, and sin not; for some have not the knowledge of God: I speak this to your shame.*

1 JOHN 1:9

9 *If we confess our sins, he is faithful and just to forgive us our sins, and to cleanse us from all unrighteousness.*

III. A Heavenly _____

PHILIPPIANS 4:13

13 *I can do all things through Christ which strengtheneth me.*

2 CORINTHIANS 9:8

8 *And God is able to make all grace abound toward you; that ye, always having all sufficiency in all things, may abound to every good work.*

PHILIPPIANS 2:13

13 *For it is God which worketh in you both to will and to do of his good pleasure.*

A. *God is _____ of our righteousness.*

1 PETER 3:12

12 *For the eyes of the Lord are over the righteous…*

2 CHRONICLES 16:9

9 *For the eyes of the LORD run to and fro throughout the whole earth, to shew himself strong in the behalf of them whose heart is perfect toward him…*

HEBREWS 6:10

10 *For God is not unrighteous to forget your work and labour of love, which ye have shewed toward his name, in that ye have ministered to the saints, and do minister.*

B. *God is _____ to our requests.*

1 PETER 3:12

12 *…and his ears are open unto their prayers…*

Psalm 91:15

15 *He shall call upon me, and I will answer him: I will be with him in trouble; I will deliver him, and honour him.*

Isaiah 58:9

9 *Then shalt thou call, and the Lord shall answer; thou shalt cry, and he shall say Here I am…*

John 15:7

7 *If ye abide in me, and my words abide in you, ye shall ask what ye will, and it shall be done unto you.*

C. God is _____ by our rebellion.

1 Peter 3:12

12 *…but the face of the Lord is against them that do evil.*

Ecclesiastes 12:13–14

13 *Let us hear the conclusion of the whole matter: Fear God, and keep his commandments: for this is the whole duty of man.*

14 *For God shall bring every work into judgment, with every secret thing, whether it be good, or whether it be evil.*

Ezekiel 7:3–4

3 *Now is the end come upon thee, and I will send mine anger upon thee, and will judge thee according to thy ways, and will recompense upon thee all thine abominations.*

4 *And mine eye shall not spare thee, neither will I have pity: but I will recompense thy ways upon thee, and thine abominations shall be in the midst of thee: and ye shall know that I am the Lord.*

1 Samuel 15:22–23

22 *And Samuel said, Hath the Lord as great delight in burnt offerings and sacrifices, as in obeying the voice of the Lord? Behold, to obey is better than sacrifice, and to hearken than the fat of rams.*

23 *For rebellion is as the sin of witchcraft, and stubbornness is as iniquity and idolatry. Because thou hast rejected the word of the Lord, he hath also rejected thee from being king.*

Conclusion

_____

_____

_____

Study Questions

1. What is the attribute that attracts us to God?

2. What is God's first institution established in Genesis 2?

3. What relationship is a portrait of God's love for us?

4. What steps can you take to strengthen your marriage against Satan's attacks?

5. What two things can you do for someone who is away from the Lord?

6. When is the best time to deal with a problem?

7. Is there a relationship you need to set right this week? If so, what actions are you going to take to restore that relationship?

8. What is the best thing you can do to help keep your spirit toward others right?

Memory Verse

ECCLESIASTES 12:13

13 *Let us hear the conclusion of the whole matter: Fear God, and keep his commandments: for this is the whole duty of man.*

An Anointed Perseverance

Text

1 Peter 3:13–22

13   And who is he that will harm you, if ye be followers of that which is good?

14   But and if ye suffer for righteousness' sake, happy are ye: and be not afraid of their terror, neither be troubled;

15   But sanctify the Lord God in your hearts: and be ready always to give an answer to every man that asketh you a reason of the hope that is in you with meekness and fear:

16   Having a good conscience; that, whereas they speak evil of you, as of evildoers, they may be ashamed that falsely accuse your good conversation in Christ.

17   For it is better, if the will of God be so, that ye suffer for well doing, than for evil doing.

18   For Christ also hath once suffered for sins, the just for the unjust, that he might bring us to God, being put to death in the flesh, but quickened by the Spirit:

19   By which also he went and preached unto the spirits in prison;

20 Which sometime were disobedient, when once the longsuffering of God waited in the days of Noah, while the ark was a preparing, wherein few, that is, eight souls were saved by water.

21   The like figure whereunto even baptism doth also now save us (not the putting away of the filth of the flesh, but the answer of a good conscience toward God,) by the resurrection of Jesus Christ:

22 Who is gone into heaven, and is on the right hand of God; angels and authorities and powers being made subject unto him.

Overview

When you think of the words *walk, pilgrimage, journey,* or *war,* you think of something that lasts a while in duration. Adversity and trouble may come upon us quickly, but they are not usually dissolved quickly. The death of a loved one, the loss of a job, a divorce, a financial hardship, a disease, all have long-lasting ramifications. Faithfulness is not measured in days but in decades!

Lesson Theme

More impressive than results is resilience. The faster the better is the way we like things, but God is interested in faithfulness. With God, patience and perseverance are admirable characteristics. God is looking for those He can count on for the long haul. Trials wear us down and Peter is going to teach us in these verses how to stay strong in the midst of the battle and persevere to victory.

Introduction

_____

_____

_____

GALATIANS 6:17

17 ...for I bear in my body the marks of the Lord Jesus.

2 TIMOTHY 4:7–8

7 I have fought a good fight, I have finished my course, I have kept the faith:

8 Henceforth there is laid up for me a crown of righteousness, which the Lord, the righteous judge shall give me at that day: and not to me only, but unto all them also that love his appearing.

I. Our _____ in Suffering

HEBREWS 13:5–6

5 Let your conversation be without covetousness: and be content with such things as ye have: for he hath said, I will never leave thee, nor forsake thee.

6 So that we may boldly say, The Lord is my helper, and I will not fear what man shall do unto me.

PSALM 3:3–6

3 But thou, O LORD, art a shield for me; my glory, and the lifter up of my head.

4 I cried unto the LORD with my voice, and he heard me out of his holy hill. Selah.

5 I laid me down and slept; I awaked; for the LORD sustained me.

6   *I will not be afraid of ten thousands of people, that have set themselves against me round about.*

PSALM 20:7

7   *Some trust in chariots, and some in horses: but we will remember the name of the LORD our God.*

A. *Jehovah is our* _____.

1 PETER 3:13

13   *And who is he that will harm you…*

ISAIAH 41:10

10   *Fear thou not; for I am with thee: be not dismayed; for I am thy God: I will strengthen thee; yea, I will help thee; yea, I will uphold thee with the right hand of my righteousness.*

ISAIAH 43:1–3

1   *…Fear not: for I have redeemed thee, I have called thee by thy name; thou art mine.*

2   *When thou passest through the waters, I will be with thee; and through the rivers, they shall not overflow thee: when thou walkest through the fire, thou shalt not be burned; neither shall the flame kindle upon thee.*

3   *For I am the LORD thy God, the Holy One of Israel…*

PSALM 27:1–5

1   *The LORD is my light and my salvation; whom shall I fear? the LORD is the strength of my life; of whom shall I be afraid?*

2   *When the wicked, even mine enemies and my foes, came upon me to eat up my flesh, they stumbled and fell.*

3   Though an host should encamp against me, my heart shall not fear: though war should rise against me, in this will I be confident.

4   One thing have I desired of the LORD, that will I seek after; that I may dwell in the house of the LORD all the days of my life, to behold the beauty of the LORD, and to enquire in his temple.

5   For in the time of trouble he shall hide me in his pavilion: in the secret of his tabernacle shall he hide me; he shall set me up upon a rock.

B. Journey with His _____.

1 PETER 3:13

13   …if ye be followers of that which is good?

PSALM 119:133

133 Order my steps in thy word: and let not any iniquity have dominion over me.

ROMANS 8:28

28   And we know that all things work together for good to them that love God, to them who are the called according to his purpose.

PSALM 34:19

19   Many are the afflictions of the righteous: but the LORD delivereth him out of them all.

C. Joy can be our _____.

1 PETER 3:14

14   But and if ye suffer for righteousness' sake, happy are ye: and be not afraid of their terror, neither be troubled.

2 Corinthians 12:7–10

7   *And lest I should be exalted above measure through the abundance of the revelations, there was given to me a thorn in the flesh, the messenger of Satan to buffet me, lest I should be exalted above measure.*

8   *For this thing I besought the Lord thrice, that it might depart from me.*

9   *And he said unto me, My grace is sufficient for thee: for my strength is made perfect in weakness. Most gladly therefore will I rather glory in my infirmities, that the power of Christ may rest upon me.*

10   *Therefore I take pleasure in infirmities, in reproaches, in necessities, in persecutions, in distresses for Christ's sake: for when I am weak, then am I strong.*

Acts 20:22–24

22   *And now, behold, I go bound in the spirit unto Jerusalem, not knowing the things that shall befall me there:*

23   *Save that the Holy Ghost witnesseth in every city, saying that bonds and afflictions abide me.*

24   *But none of these things move me, neither count I my life dear unto myself, so that I might finish my course with joy, and the ministry, which I have received of the Lord Jesus, to testify the gospel of the grace of God.*

II. Our _____ in Suffering

A. A personal _____

1 Peter 3:15

15   *But sanctify the Lord God in your hearts...*

PROVERBS 4:23

23 Keep thy heart with all diligence; for out of it are the issues of life.

LUKE 6:45

45 A good man out of the good treasure of his heart bringeth forth that which is good; and an evil man out of the evil treasure of his heart bringeth forth that which is evil: for of the abundance of the heart his mouth speaketh.

B. A proper _____

1 PETER 3:15

15 ...and be ready always to give an answer to every man that asketh you a reason of the hope that is in you with meekness and fear:

2 TIMOTHY 2:15

15 Study to shew thyself approved unto God, a workman that needeth not to be ashamed, rightly dividing the word of truth.

ACTS 4:20

20 For we cannot but speak the things which we have seen and heard.

2 CORINTHIANS 4:13

13 We having the same spirit of faith, according as it is written, I believed, and therefore have I spoken; we also believe, and therefore speak.

C. A poor _____

1 PETER 3:16

16   *Having a good conscience; that whereas they speak evil of you, as evildoers, they may be ashamed that falsely accuse your good conversation in Christ.*

ACTS 23:1

1   *And Paul, earnestly beholding the council, said, Men and brethren, I have lived in all good conscience before God until this day.*

ACTS 24:16

16   *And herein do I exercise myself, to have always a conscience void of offence toward God, and toward men.*

2 CORINTHIANS 1:12

12   *For our rejoicing is this, the testimony of our conscience, that in simplicity and godly sincerity, not with fleshly wisdom, but by the grace of God, we have had our conversation in the world, and more abundantly to you-ward.*

D. A pleasing _____

1 PETER 3:17

17   *For it is better, if the will of God be so, that ye suffer for well doing, than for evil doing.*

MATTHEW 6:33

33   *But seek ye first the kingdom of God, and his righteousness; and all these things shall be added unto you.*

1 SAMUEL 3:18

18   *And Samuel told him every whit, and hid nothing from him. And he said, It is the LORD: let him do what seemeth him good.*

III. Our _____ for Suffering

2 TIMOTHY 1:9

9 Who hath saved us, and called us with an holy calling, not according to our works, but according to his own purpose and grace, which was given us in Christ Jesus before the world began.

A. A superior _____

1 PETER 3:18–21

18 For Christ also hath once suffered for sins, the just for the unjust, that he might bring us to God, being put to death in the flesh, but quickened by the Spirit:

19 By which also he went and preached unto the spirits in prison;

20 Which sometime were disobedient, when once the longsuffering of God waited in the days of Noah, while the ark was a preparing, wherein few, that is, eight souls were saved by water.

21 The like figure whereunto even baptism doth also now save us (not the putting away of the filth of the flesh, but the answer of a good conscience toward God,) by the resurrection of Jesus Christ:

ACTS 7:58

58 And cast him out of the city, and stoned him: and the witnesses laid down their clothes at a young man's feet, whose name was Saul.

ACTS 9:4–5

4 And he fell to the earth, and heard a voice saying unto him, Saul, Saul, why persecutest thou me?

5 And he said, Who art thou, Lord?…

B. A sterling _____

1 PETER 3:22

22 Who is gone into heaven, and is on the right hand of God; angels and authorities and powers being made subject unto him.

Conclusion

_____

_____

_____

Study Questions

1. What is crucial to remember when passing through a fiery trial?

2. If we are daily walking with God, why can we rejoice no matter our circumstances?

3. How has God used a trial to shape you?

4. What is the outcome of your life a direct result of?

5. You cannot control the actions of life or others around you, but what can you control?

6. In order for God to use you in your trial, with what should you be filling your heart and mind?

7. Even when it doesn't seem logical, what do we need to remember about God's plan?

8. Take a moment and write out some blessings that have come as a result from trials in your life.

Memory Verse

ROMANS 8:28

28 And we know that all things work together for good to them that love God, to them who are the called according to his purpose.

An Alluring Perversion

Text

1 PETER 4:1–11

1   Forasmuch then as Christ hath suffered for us in the flesh, arm yourselves likewise with the same mind: for he that hath suffered in the flesh hath ceased from sin;

2   That he no longer should live the rest of his time in the flesh to the lusts of men, but to the will of God.

3   For the time past of our life may suffice us to have wrought the will of the Gentiles, when we walked in lasciviousness, lusts, excess of wine, revellings, banquetings, and abominable idolatries:

4   Wherein they think it strange that ye run not with them to the same excess of riot, speaking evil of you:

5   Who shall give account to him that is ready to judge the quick and the dead.

6   For for this cause was the gospel preached also to them that are dead, that they might be judged according to men in the flesh, but live according to God in the spirit.

7   But the end of all things is at hand: be ye therefore sober, and watch unto prayer.

8   And above all things have fervent charity among yourselves: for charity shall cover the multitude of sins.

9   Use hospitality one to another without grudging.

10   As every man hath received the gift, even so minister the same one to another, as good stewards of the manifold grace of God.

11   If any man speak, let him speak as the oracles of God; if any man minister, let him do it as of the ability which God giveth:

that God in all things may be glorified through Jesus Christ, to whom be praise and dominion for ever and ever. Amen.

Overview

With the previous lessons in mind, Satan wants to stop us at all costs. He knows that our trials will produce fruit for eternity in our lives and will impact others. He will do whatever is necessary to put an end to our testimonies. He works hard during times of difficulty because he knows that it is an opportunity to cause us to lose our focus. If God's people fail in times of adversity, all the devil has to do is point the lost to that failure. When Christianity doesn't work in difficulty, the unsaved wonder if it works at all.

Lesson Theme

Peter has laid the groundwork thus far for a victorious life in the midst of trials, and now encourages the reader to "stay the course." Trials have a way of wearing us down. We begin to wonder if we are all alone in the battle or if anyone else cares that we are suffering. The Apostle admonishes us not to quit but to stay true to what we have learned, knowing that the devil will keep firing his darts in our direction.

Introduction

_____

_____

_____

2 Corinthians 11:3

3   But I fear, lest by any means, as the serpent beguiled Eve through his subtilty, so your minds should be corrupted from the simplicity that is in Christ.

1 Thessalonians 3:5

5   For this cause, when I could no longer forbear, I sent to know your faith, lest by some means the tempter have tempted you, and our labour be in vain.

I.   Stay _____

Ephesians 6:10–18

10   Finally, my brethren, be strong in the Lord, and in the power of his might.

11   Put on the whole armour of God, that ye may be able to stand against the wiles of the devil.

12   For we wrestle not against flesh and blood, but against principalities, against powers, against the rulers of the darkness of this world, against spiritual wickedness in high places.

13   Wherefore take unto you the whole armour of God, that ye may be able to withstand in the evil day, and having done all, to stand.

14   Stand therefore, having your loins girt about with truth, and having on the breastplate of righteousness;

15   And your feet shod with the preparation of the gospel of peace;

16 *Above all, taking the shield of faith, wherewith ye shall be able to quench all the fiery darts of the wicked.*

17 *And take the helmet of salvation, and the sword of the Spirit, which is the word of God:*

18 *Praying always with all prayer and supplication in the Spirit, and watching thereunto with all perseverance and supplication for all saints;*

A. A _____ *Master*

1 PETER 4:1

1 *Forasmuch then as Christ hath suffered for us in the flesh…*

HEBREWS 4:15

15 *For we have not an high priest which cannot be touched with the feeling of our infirmities; but was in all points tempted like as we are, yet without sin.*

2 CORINTHIANS 5:21

21 *For he hath made him to be sin for us, who knew no sin; that we might be made the righteousness of God in him.*

B. A _____ *mind*

1 PETER 4:1

1 *…arm yourselves likewise with the same mind: for he that hath suffered in the flesh hath ceased from sin.*

ROMANS 8:6

6 *For to be carnally minded is death; but to be spiritually minded is life and peace.*

PHILIPPIANS 2:5

5 *Let this mind be in you, which was also in Christ Jesus.*

PHILIPPIANS 4:8

8   *Finally, brethren, whatsoever things are true, whatsoever things are honest, whatsoever things are just, whatsoever things are pure, whatsoever things are lovely, whatsoever things are of good report; if there be any virtue, and if there be any praise, think on these things.*

2 CORINTHIANS 10:5

5   *Casting down imaginations, and every high thing that exalteth itself against the knowledge of God, and bringing into captivity every thought to the obedience of Christ.*

II. Stay _____

ACTS 26:16

16   *But rise, and stand upon thy feet: for I have appeared unto thee for this purpose, to make thee a minister and a witness both of these things which thou hast seen, and of those things in the which I will appear unto thee.*

2 TIMOTHY 4:7

7   *I have fought a good fight, I have finished my course, I have kept the faith.*

EPHESIANS 3:11

11   *According to the eternal purpose which he purposed in Christ Jesus our Lord.*

A. A _____ of time

1 PETER 4:2

2   *That he no longer should live the rest of his time in the flesh to the lusts of men…*

HEBREWS 11:25

25 ...*to enjoy the pleasures of sin for a season.*

PSALM 16:11

11 *Thou wilt shew me the path of life: in thy presence is fulness of joy; at thy right hand there are pleasures for evermore.*

B. A _____ target

1 PETER 4:2

2 ...*but to the will of God.*

PSALM 40:8

8 *I delight to do thy will, O my God: yea, thy law is within my heart.*

PSALM 143:10

10 *Teach me to do thy will: for thou art my God: thy spirit is good; lead me into the land of uprightness.*

III. Stay _____

PSALM 62:2

2 *He only is my rock and my salvation, he is my defence, I shall not be greatly moved.*

PSALM 16:8

8 *I have set the LORD always before me: because he is at my right hand, I shall not be moved.*

A. _____ past associations.

1 PETER 4:3

3 *For the time past of our life may suffice us to have wrought the will of the Gentiles, when we walked in*

lasciviousness, lusts, excess of wine, revellings, banqueting, and abominable idolatries.

GALATIANS 5:7

7   Ye did run well; who did hinder you that ye should not obey the truth?

PROVERBS 4:14

14   Enter not into the path of the wicked, and go not in the way of evil men.

PROVERBS 24:1

1   Be not thou envious against evil men, neither desire to be with them.

2 CORINTHIANS 6:14

14   Be ye not unequally yoked together with unbelievers: for what fellowship hath righteousness with unrighteousness? and what communion hath light with darkness?

B. Get _____ to present accusations.

1 PETER 4:4

Wherein they think it strange that ye run not with them to the same excess of riot, speaking evil of you.

PSALM 31:13

13   For I have heard the slander of many: fear was on every side: while they took counsel together against me, they devised to take away my life.

PROVERBS 11:9

9   An hypocrite with his mouth destroyeth his neighbour: but through knowledge shall the just be delivered.

JEREMIAH 9:4

4   Take ye heed every one of his neighbour, and trust ye not in any brother: for every brother will utterly supplant, and every neighbour will walk with slanders.

C. Be _____ of a future accountability.

1 PETER 4:5–6

5   Who shall give an account to him that is ready to judge the quick and the dead.

6   For for this cause was the gospel preached also to them that are dead, that they might be judged according to men in the flesh, but live according to God in the spirit.

1 CORINTHIANS 3:13

13   Every man's work shall be made manifest: for the day shall declare it, because it shall be revealed by fire; and the fire shall try every man's work of what sort it is.

ROMANS 14:10–12

10   But why dost thou judge thy brother? or why dost thou set at nought thy brother? for we shall all stand before the judgment seat of Christ.

11   For it is written, As I live, saith the Lord, every knee shall bow to me, and every tongue shall confess to God.

12   So then every one of us shall give account of himself to God.

IV. Stay _____

LUKE 2:52

52   And Jesus increased in wisdom and stature, and in favour with God and man.

Acts 2:46–47

46 *And they, continuing daily with one accord in the temple, and breaking bread from house to house, did eat their meat with gladness and singleness of heart,*

47 *Praising God, and having favour with all the people. And the Lord added to the church daily such as should be saved.*

A. A _____ *communication*

1 Peter 4:7

7 *But the end of all things is at hand: be ye therefore sober, and watch unto prayer.*

Proverbs 16:7

7 *When a man's ways please the LORD, he maketh even his enemies to be at peace with him.*

B. A _____ *charity*

1 Peter 4:8–10

8 *And above all things have fervent charity among yourselves: for charity shall cover the multitude of sins.*

9 *Use hospitality one to another without grudging.*

10 *As every man hath received the gift, even so minister the same one to another, as good stewards of the manifold grace of God.*

Ephesians 4:32

32 *And be ye kind one to another, tenderhearted, forgiving one another, even as God for Christ's sake hath forgiven you.*

Colossians 3:13

13 *Forbearing one another, and forgiving one another, if any man have a quarrel against any: even as Christ forgave you, so also do ye.*

MATTHEW 18:23–33

23   Therefore is the kingdom of heaven likened unto a certain king, which would take account of his servants.

24   And when he had begun to reckon, one was brought unto him, which owed him ten thousand talents.

25   But forasmuch as he had not to pay, his lord commanded him to be sold, and his wife, and children, and all that he had, and payment to be made.

26   The servant therefore fell down, and worshipped him, saying, Lord, have patience with me, and I will pay thee all.

27   Then the lord of that servant was moved with compassion, and loosed him, and forgave him the debt.

28   But the same servant went out, and found one of his fellowservants, which owed him an hundred pence: and he laid hands on him, and took him by the throat, saying, Pay me that thou owest.

29   And his fellowservant fell down at his feet, and besought him, saying, Have patience with me, and I will pay thee all.

30   And he would not: but went and cast him into prison, till he should pay the debt.

31   So when his fellowservants saw what was done, they were very sorry, and came and told unto their lord all that was done.

32   Then his lord, after that he had called him, said unto him, O thou wicked servant, I forgave thee all that debt, because thou desiredst me:

33   Shouldest not thou also have had compassion on thy fellowservant, even as I had pity on thee?

C. A _____ *cooperation*

1 PETER 4:11

11   If any man speak, let him speak as the oracles of God; if any man minister, let him do it as of the ability which God

giveth; that God in all things may be glorified through Jesus Christ, to whom be praise and dominion for ever and ever. Amen.

Colossians 1:29

29 Whereunto I also labour, striving according to his working, which worketh in me mightily.

1 Corinthians 3:5–9

5 Who then is Paul, and who is Apollos, but ministers by whom ye believed, even as the Lord gave to every man?
6 I have planted, Apollos watered; but God gave the increase.
7 So then neither is he that planteth any thing, neither he that watereth; but God that giveth the increase.
8 Now he that planteth and he that watereth are one: and every man shall receive his own reward according to his own labour.
9 For we are labourers together with God...

Conclusion

_____

_____

_____

Study Questions

1. Who was victorious in every test He faced and whose example we should follow?

2. If Satan can infiltrate our thinking, what will he be able to infect?

3. Why should we have some righteous stubbornness?

4. Whom should we be careful about that can hinder us from finishing our race?

5. When God's Word moves forward, what should we expect?

6. According to Daniel Webster, what is the greatest thought that can occupy a man's mind?

7. Does your behavior in trials attract others to your belief? Why or why not?

8. When we forget what God has done for us, what else will we forget?

Memory Verse

PSALM 16:11

11 *Thou wilt shew me the path of life: in thy presence is fulness of joy; at thy right hand there are pleasures for evermore.*

An Appointed Persecution

Text

1 PETER 4:12–19

12 Beloved, think it not strange concerning the fiery trial which is to try you, as though some strange thing happened unto you:

13 But rejoice, inasmuch as ye are partakers of Christ's sufferings; that, when his glory shall be revealed, ye may be glad also with exceeding joy.

14 If ye be reproached for the name of Christ, happy are ye; for the spirit of glory and of God resteth upon you: on their part he is evil spoken of, but on your part he is glorified.

15 But let none of you suffer as a murderer, or as a thief, or as an evildoer, or as a busybody in other men's matters.

16 Yet if any man suffer as a Christian, let him not be ashamed; but let him glorify God on this behalf.

17 For the time is come that judgment must begin at the house of God: and if it first begin at us, what shall the end be of them that obey not the gospel of God?

18 And if the righteous scarcely be saved, where shall the ungodly and the sinner appear?

19 Wherefore let them that suffer according to the will of God commit the keeping of their souls to him in well doing, as unto a faithful Creator.

Overview

In America, we become very alarmed when any kind of religious persecution comes our way. Throughout much of history, persecution was the norm for most of Christianity. We have been very fortunate to live in a country that has upheld religious freedom. That could change in the years ahead as we see atheism grow and laws change. However, whenever there has been persecution, the church has grown. It is all part of God's plan, and we must embrace the challenge and rest in the promises of God's Word no matter what comes our way.

Lesson Theme

No one prays for trials or persecution, but they are a part of the Christian life. We love the promises that God gives us in His Word, but some of those promises are negative as well. *"Yea, and all that will live godly in Christ Jesus shall suffer persecution"* (2 Timothy 3:12). God promises that difficult times will come, but reminds us that through them all, He does not change! We can still trust Him in the difficult times—in fact, they are designed to increase our faith rather than destroy it.

Introduction

_____

_____

_____

LUKE 14:27

27 *And whosoever doth not bear his cross, and come after me, cannot be my disciple.*

2 SAMUEL 24:24

24 *And the king said unto Araunah, Nay; but I will surely buy it of thee at a price: neither will I offer burnt offerings unto the LORD my God of that which doth cost me nothing...*

I. An Expected _____

2 TIMOTHY 3:12

12 *Yea, and all that will live godly in Christ Jesus shall suffer persecution.*

A. Don't be _____ by a tested life.

1 PETER 4:12

12 *Beloved, think it not strange concerning the fiery trial which is to try you, as though some strange thing happened unto you.*

PSALM 17:3

3 *Thou hast proved mine heart; thou hast visited me in the night; thou hast tried me, and shalt find nothing: I am purposed that my mouth shall not transgress.*

ZECHARIAH 13:9

9   And I will bring the third part through the fire, and will refine them as silver is refined, and will try them as gold is tried: they shall call on my name, and I will hear them: I will say, It is my people: and they shall say, The LORD is my God.

B. Don't be _____ of a true love.

1 PETER 4:12

12   Beloved…

JEREMIAH 31:3

3   The LORD hath appeared of old unto me, saying, Yea, I have loved thee with an everlasting love: therefore with lovingkindness have I drawn thee.

ISAIAH 54:10

10   For the mountains shall depart, and the hills be removed; but my kindness shall not depart from thee, neither shall the covenant of my peace be removed, saith the LORD that hath mercy on thee.

ROMANS 8:35

35   Who shall separate us from the love of Christ? shall tribulation, or distress, or persecution, or famine, or nakedness, or peril, or sword?

II. An Exciting _____

MATTHEW 11:28–30

28   Come unto me, all ye that labour and are heavy laden, and I will give you rest.

29 Take my yoke upon you, and learn of me; for I am meek and lowly of heart: and ye shall find rest unto your souls.
30 For my yoke is easy, and my burden is light.

A. A unique _____

1 PETER 4:13

13 But rejoice, inasmuch as ye are partakers of Christ's sufferings...

HEBREWS 13:12–14

12 Wherefore Jesus also, that he might sanctify the people with his own blood, suffered without the gate.
13 Let us go forth therefore unto him without the camp, bearing his reproach.
14 For here have we no continuing city, but we seek one to come.

GALATIANS 2:20

20 I am crucified with Christ: nevertheless I live; yet not I, but Christ liveth in me: and the life which I now live in the flesh I live by the faith of the Son of God, who loved me, and gave himself for me.

2 CORINTHIANS 4:11

11 For we which live are alway delivered unto death for Jesus' sake, that the life also of Jesus might be made manifest in our mortal flesh.

B. An ultimate _____

1 PETER 4:13–14

13 ...that, when his glory shall be revealed, ye may be glad also with exceeding joy.

14 If ye be reproached for the name of Christ, happy are ye…

JOHN 13:17

17 If ye know these things, happy are ye if ye do them.

ACTS 5:40–42

40 And to him they agreed: and when they had called the apostles, and beaten them, they commanded that they should not speak in the name of Jesus, and let them go.

41 And they departed from the presence of the council, rejoicing that they were counted worthy to suffer shame for his name.

42 And daily in the temple, and in every house, they ceased not to teach and preach Jesus Christ.

C. An untarnished _____

1 PETER 4:14

4 …for the spirit of glory and of God resteth upon you: on their part he is evil spoken of, but on your part he is glorified.

JOHN 1:6–8

6 There was a man sent from God, whose name was John.

7 The same came for a witness, to bear witness of the Light, that all men through him might believe.

8 He was not that Light, but was sent to bear witness of that Light.

ROMANS 8:17

17 And if children, then heirs; heirs of God, and joint-heirs with Christ; if so be that we suffer with him, that we may be also glorified together.

III. An Exception _____

A. Refrain from _____ acts.

1 PETER 4:15
15 But let none of you suffer as a murderer, or as a thief, or as an evildoer...

PSALM 34:16
16 The face of the LORD is against them that do evil...

PROVERBS 14:34
34 Righteousness exalteth a nation: but sin is a reproach to any people.

B. Refrain from _____ activity.

1 PETER 4:15
15 ...or as a busybody in other men's matters.

PROVERBS 6:16, 19
16 These six things doth the LORD hate: yea, seven are an abomination unto him.
19 A false witness that speaketh lies, and he that soweth discord among the brethren.

2 THESSALONIANS 3:11
11 For we hear that there are some which walk among you disorderly, working not at all, but are busybodies.

1 TIMOTHY 5:13
13 And withal they learn to be idle, wandering about from house to house; and not only idle, but tattlers also and busybodies, speaking things which they ought not.

IV. An Early _____

1 CORINTHIANS 11:31

31 For if we would judge ourselves, we should not be judged.

A. A daily preparation for the _____

1 PETER 4:17

17 For the time is come that judgment must begin at the house of God…

JOHN 15:3

3 Now ye are clean through the word which I have spoken unto you.

PROVERBS 28:13

13 He that covereth his sins shall not prosper: but whoso confesseth and forsaketh them shall have mercy.

1 JOHN 1:9

9 If we confess our sins, he is faithful and just to forgive us our sins, and to cleanse us from all unrighteousness.

2 TIMOTHY 2:19–21

19 Nevertheless the foundation of God standeth sure, having this seal, The Lord knoweth them that are his. And, Let every one that nameth the name of Christ depart from iniquity.

20 But in a great house there are not only vessels of gold and of silver, but also of wood and of earth; and some to honour, and some to dishonour.

21 If a man therefore purge himself from these, he shall be a vessel unto honour, sanctified, and meet for the master's use, and prepared unto every good work.

B. A devastating punishment for the _____

1 PETER 4:17–18

17 …and if it first begin at us, what shall the end be of them that obey not the gospel of God?

18 And if the righteous scarcely be saved, where shall the ungodly and the sinner appear?

1 JOHN 5:11–12

11 And this is the record, that God hath given to us eternal life, and this life is in his Son.

12 He that hath the Son hath life; and he that hath not the Son of God hath not life.

JOHN 3:36

36 He that believeth on the Son hath everlasting life: and he that believeth not the Son shall not see life; but the wrath of God abideth on him.

ROMANS 1:18–20

18 For the wrath of God is revealed from heaven against all ungodliness and unrighteousness of men, who hold the truth in unrighteousness;

19 Because that which may be known of God is manifest in them; for God hath shewed it unto them.

20 For the invisible things of him from the creation of the world are clearly seen, being understood by the things that are made, even his eternal power and Godhead; so that they are without excuse.

C. A divine protection for the _____

1 PETER 4:19

19 Wherefore let them that suffer according to the will of God commit the keeping of their souls to him in well doing, as unto a faithful Creator.

EPHESIANS 1:13–14

13 *In whom ye also trusted, after that ye heard the word of truth, the gospel of your salvation: in whom also after that ye believed, ye were sealed with that holy Spirit of promise.*

14 *Which is the earnest of our inheritance until the redemption of the purchased possession, unto the praise of his glory.*

REVELATION 22:4

4 *And they shall see his face; and his name shall be in their foreheads.*

Conclusion

_____

_____

_____

Study Questions

1. According to 2 Timothy 3:12, who suffers persecution?

2. What type of love does God have toward us?

3. What are some things we receive from God the moment we accept Him?

4. How can you enjoy bearing burdens with Christ?

5. How does God truly refine us?

6. When we suffer and bear a trial like Christ, what are we reflecting?

7. How can you keep your vessel clean and ready for God's use?

8. Are you willing to suffer persecution for Christ's sake? Why or why not?

Memory Verse

GALATIANS 2:20

20 I am crucified with Christ: nevertheless I live; yet not I, but Christ liveth in me: and the life which I now live in the flesh I live by the faith of the Son of God, who loved me, and gave himself for me.

An Abiding Pillar

Text

1 PETER 5:1–14

1   The elders which are among you I exhort, who am also an elder, and a witness of the sufferings of Christ, and also a partaker of the glory that shall be revealed:

2   Feed the flock of God which is among you, taking the oversight thereof, not by constraint, but willingly; not for filthy lucre, but of a ready mind;

3   Neither as being lords over God's heritage, but being ensamples to the flock.

4   And when the chief Shepherd shall appear, ye shall receive a crown of glory that fadeth not away.

5   Likewise, ye younger, submit yourselves unto the elder. Yea, all of you be subject one to another, and be clothed with humility: for God resisteth the proud, and giveth grace to the humble.

6   Humble yourselves therefore under the mighty hand of God, that he may exalt you in due time:

7   Casting all your care upon him; for he careth for you.

8   Be sober, be vigilant; because your adversary the devil, as a roaring lion, walketh about, seeking whom he may devour:

9   Whom resist stedfast in the faith, knowing that the same afflictions are accomplished in your brethren that are in the world.

10   But the God of all grace, who hath called us unto his eternal glory by Christ Jesus, after that ye have suffered a while, make you perfect, stablish, strengthen, settle you.

11   To him be glory and dominion for ever and ever. Amen.

12   *By Silvanus, a faithful brother unto you, as I suppose, I have written briefly, exhorting, and testifying that this is the true grace of God wherein ye stand.*

13   *The church that is at Babylon, elected together with you, saluteth you; and so doth Marcus my son.*

14   *Greet ye one another with a kiss of charity. Peace be with you all that are in Christ Jesus. Amen.*

Overview

The local church is God's vehicle for carrying out the Great Commission. How sad to see many people abandoning the local church. Even sadder is the fact that many churches have lost their vision to minister to God's people and reach the lost. God intended the church to be the "pillar and ground of truth." How we need that foundation to be steadfast and unmovable today. God's plan still works and His plan includes the local church. He has promised His power, protection, and provision.

Lesson Theme

Much of what Peter has shared in this epistle has come from his own experience in trials. Now as he closes the letter, he wants to make sure that the reader continues in the truth. No one can survive without the ministry of the local church. God has set it up that way and we are wise to keep that landmark entrenched in our lives and society. Peter will teach us here the importance of following the Chief Shepherd and the undershepherd—the pastor.

Introduction

_____

_____

_____

MATTHEW 16:18
18 ...I will build my church; and the gates of hell shall not prevail against it.

I. A _____ Leadership

A. Pastors must accurately _____.

1 PETER 5:1–2
1   The elders which are among you I exhort, who am also an elder, and a witness of the sufferings of Christ, and also a partaker of the glory that shall be revealed:
2   Feed the flock of God which is among you, taking the oversight thereof...

JEREMIAH 3:15
15   And I will give you pastors according to mine heart, which shall feed you with knowledge and understanding.

ACTS 20:28
28   Take heed therefore unto yourselves, and to all the flock, over the which the Holy Ghost hath made you overseers, to feed the church of God, which he hath purchased with his own blood.

B. Pastors must avoid _____.

1 Peter 5:2

2 ...*not by constraint, but willingly; nor for filthy lucre, but of a ready mind.*

Ephesians 3:7–8

7 *Whereof I was made a minister, according to the gift of the grace of God given unto me by the effectual working of his power.*

8 *Unto me, who am less than the least of all saints, is this grace given, that I should preach among the Gentiles the unsearchable riches of Christ.*

1 Timothy 3:1–3

1 *This is a true saying, If a man desire the office of a bishop, he desireth a good work.*

2 *A bishop then must be blameless, the husband of one wife, vigilant, sober, of good behavior, given to hospitality, apt to teach;*

3 *Not given to wine, no striker, not greedy of filthy lucre; but patient, not a brawler, not covetous.*

C. Pastors must always _____.

1 Peter 5:3

3 *Neither as being lords over God's heritage, but being ensamples to the flock.*

2 Thessalonians 3:9

9 *Not because we have not power, but to make ourselves an ensample unto you to follow us.*

1 Timothy 4:12

12 *Let no man despise thy youth; but be thou an example of the believers, in word, in conversation, in charity, in spirit, in faith, in purity.*

Titus 2:7

7   In all things shewing thyself a pattern of good works: in doctrine shewing uncorruptness, gravity, sincerity.

D. Pastors will be acknowledged for their _____.

1 Peter 5:4

4   And when the Chief Shepherd shall appear, ye shall receive a crown of glory that fadeth not away.

Revelation 22:12

12   And, behold, I come quickly; and my reward is with me, to give every man according as his work shall be.

II. A _____ Laity

1 Corinthians 11:1

1   Be ye followers of me, even as I also am of Christ.

A. A requirement of _____

1 Peter 5:5–6

5   Likewise, ye younger, submit yourselves unto the elder. Yea, all of you be subject one to another, and be clothed with humility: for God resisteth the proud, and giveth grace to the humble.

6   Humble yourselves therefore under the mighty hand of God, that he may exalt you in due time.

Hebrews 13:7

7   Remember them which have the rule over you, who have spoken unto you the word of God: whose faith follow, considering the end of their conversation.

HEBREWS 13:17

17   *Obey them that have the rule over you, and submit yourselves: for they watch for your souls, as they that must give account, that they may do it with joy, and not with grief: for that is unprofitable for you.*

B.   *A recognition of* _____

1 PETER 5:7

7   *Casting all your care upon him; for he careth for you.*

PSALM 115:12

12   *The LORD hath been mindful of us: he will bless us…*

MATTHEW 6:25–32

25   *Therefore I say unto you, Take no thought for your life, what ye shall eat, or what ye shall drink; nor yet for your body, what ye shall put on. Is not the life more than meat, and the body than raiment?*

26   *Behold the fowls of the air: for they sow not, neither do they reap, nor gather into barns; yet your heavenly Father feedeth them. Are ye not much better than they?*

27   *Which of you by taking thought can add one cubit unto his stature?*

28   *And why take ye thought for raiment? Consider the lilies of the field, how they grow; they toil not, neither do they spin:*

29   *And yet I say unto you, That even Solomon in all his glory was not arrayed like one of these.*

30   *Wherefore, if God so clothe the grass of the field, which to day is, and to morrow is cast into the oven, shall he not much more clothe you, O ye of little faith?*

31   *Therefore take no thought, saying, What shall we eat? or, What shall we drink? or, Wherewithal shall we be clothed?*

32 *(For after all these things do the Gentiles seek:) for your heavenly Father knoweth that ye have need of all these things.*

C. A reason for _____

1 PETER 5:8

8 *Be sober, be vigilant; because your adversary the devil, as a roaring lion, walketh about, seeking whom he may devour.*

ZECHARIAH 3:1

1 *And he shewed me Joshua the high priest standing before the angel of the LORD, and Satan standing at his right hand to resist him.*

MATTHEW 13:19

19 *When any one heareth the word of the kingdom, and understandeth it not, then cometh the wicked one, and catcheth away that which was sown in his heart…*

EPHESIANS 6:12

12 *For we wrestle not against flesh and blood, but against principalities, against powers, against the rulers of the darkness of this world, against spiritual wickedness in high places.*

III. A _____ Love

JOHN 14:21–23

21 *He that hath my commandments, and keepeth them, he it is that loveth me: and he that loveth me shall be loved of my Father, and I will love him, and will manifest myself to him.*

22 *Judas saith unto him, not Iscariot, Lord, how is it that thou wilt manifest thyself unto us, and not unto the world?*
23 *Jesus answered and said unto him, If a man love me, he will keep my words: and my Father will love him, and we will come unto him, and make our abode with him.*

A. Suffering _____ the believer.

1 PETER 5:10

10 *But the God of all grace, who hath called us unto his eternal glory by Christ Jesus, after that ye have suffered a while, make you perfect…*

EPHESIANS 4:13

13 *Till we all come in the unity of the faith, and of the knowledge of the Son of God, unto a perfect man, unto the measure of the stature of the fullness of Christ.*

JAMES 1:2–4

2 *My brethren, count it all joy when ye fall into divers temptations;*
3 *Knowing this, that the trying of your faith worketh patience.*
4 *But let patience have her perfect work, that ye may be perfect and entire, wanting nothing.*

B. Suffering _____ the believer.

1 PETER 5:10

10 *…stablish…*

PSALM 40:2

2 *He brought me up also out of an horrible pit, out of the miry clay, and set my feet upon a rock, and established my goings.*

ISAIAH 54:14

14 In righteousness shalt thou be established: thou shalt be far from oppression; for thou shalt not fear: and from terror; for it shall not come near thee.

C. Suffering _____ the believer.

1 PETER 5:10

10 ...strengthen...

2 TIMOTHY 2:21

21 If a man therefore purge himself from these, he shall be a vessel unto honour, sanctified, and meet for the master's use, and prepared unto every good work.

JOB 16:12

12 I was at ease, but he hath broken me asunder: he hath also taken me by my neck, and shaken me to pieces, and set me up for his mark.

D. Suffering _____ the believer.

1 PETER 5:10

10 ...settle you.

LUKE 22:31–32

31 And the Lord said, Simon, Simon, behold, Satan hath desired to have you, that he may sift you as wheat:
32 But I have prayed for thee, that thy faith fail not: and when thou art converted, strengthen thy brethren.

Conclusion

DANIEL 3:21–25

21 Then these men were bound in their coats, their hosen, and their hats, and their other garments, and were cast into the midst of the burning fiery furnace.

22 Therefore because the king's commandment was urgent, and the furnace exceeding hot, the flame of the fire slew those men that took up Shadrach, Meshach, and Abed–nego.

23 And these three men, Shadrach, Meshach, and Abed–nego, fell down bound into the midst of the burning fiery furnace.

24 Then Nebuchadnezzar the king was astonied, and rose up in haste, and spake, and said unto his counsellors, Did not we cast three men bound into the midst of the fire? They answered and said unto the king, True, O king.

25 He answered and said, Lo, I see four men loose, walking in the midst of the fire, and they have no hurt; and the form of the fourth is like the Son of God.

ISAIAH 43:1–3

1 But now thus saith the LORD that created thee, O Jacob, and he that formed thee, O Israel, Fear not: for I have redeemed thee, I have called thee by thy name; thou art mine.

2 When thou passest through the waters, I will be with thee; and through the rivers, they shall not overflow thee: when thou walkest through the fire, thou shalt not be burned; neither shall the flame kindle upon thee.

3 For I am the LORD thy God…

Study Questions

1. What are the staples to a healthy spiritual diet?

2. What is the number one concern of a shepherd?

3. Who has God placed over us and commanded us to follow?

4. How are you actively following your pastor?

5. What is Satan's one goal?

6. In what do trials firmly root you?

7.   Why do we need to endure the furnace of trial?

8.   Why can you boldly walk through the fire?

Memory Verse

PSALM 40:2

2   *He brought me up also out of an horrible pit, out of the miry clay, and set my feet upon a rock, and established my goings.*

Striving Together
P u b l i c a t i o n s

For additional Christian
growth resources visit
www.strivingtogether.com